Exclusive Distributors:
Music Sales Limited
8-9 Frith Street,
London W1V 5TZ, England.
Music Sales Pty Limited
120 Rothschild Avenue,
Rosebery, NSW 2018, Australia.

Order No. HLE90000297
ISBN 0-7119-6456-4

Cover design by Pearce Marchbank and Ben May, Studio Twenty, London.

Printed in the USA.

Great Songs of the **Forties**

Your Guarantee of Quality

As publishers, we strive to produce every book to the highest commercial standards.
This book has been carefully designed to minimise awkward page turns and
to make playing from it a real pleasure.
Throughout, the printing and binding have been planned to ensure a sturdy,
attractive publication which should give years of enjoyment.
If your copy fails to meet our high standards,
please inform us and we will gladly replace it.

Music Sales' complete catalogue describes thousands of titles
and is available in full colour sections by subject,
direct from Music Sales Limited.
Please state your areas of interest and
send a cheque/postal order for £1.50 for postage to:
Music Sales Limited, Newmarket Road,
Bury St. Edmunds, Suffolk IP33 3YB.

Visit the Internet Music Shop at
http://www.musicsales.co.uk

FOR ORGANS, PIANOS & ELECTRONIC KEYBOARDS

8

HLE
Hal Leonard Europe
Distributed by Music Sales

A Dream Is A Wish Your Heart Makes
48

A Sunday Kind Of Love
96

Across The Alley From The Alamo
4

All Through The Day
10

Anniversary Song
14

Baby, It's Cold Outside
16

Bali Ha'i
18

Beat Me Daddy, Eight To The Bar
20

Besame Mucho (Kiss Me Much)
24

Bibbidi-Bobbidi-Boo (The Magic Song)
26

Blue Champagne
28

Boogie Woogie Bugle Boy
7

Bye Bye Baby
30

Chiquita Banana
36

Cruising Down The River
33

Day By Day
40

Diamonds Are A Girl's Best Friend
46

Don't Get Around Much Anymore
43

(I Love You) For Sentimental Reasons
50

God Bless' The Child
52

Have I Told You Lately That I Love You
54

I'll Remember April
56

I'm Beginning To See The Light
58

I've Got A Lovely Bunch Of Coconuts
60

If I Loved You
64

It Might As Well Be Spring
66

It's A Grand Night For Singing
68

It's A Most Unusual Day
70

Long Ago (And Far Away)
74

Mairzy Doats
76

Moonlight Becomes You
78

Oh, What A Beautiful Mornin'
82

Oklahoma
84

On A Slow Boat To China
90

Opus One
87

People Will Say We're In Love
92

Some Enchanted Evening
94

Take The "A" Train
98

Taking A Chance On Love
100

Tangerine
102

That Old Black Magic
104

The American Patrol
12

The Last Time I Saw Paris
72

The Nearness Of You
80

There! I've Said It Again
116

Tuxedo Junction
108

You'll Never Walk Alone
110

Younger Than Springtime
112

Zip-A-Dee-Doo-Dah
114

Registration Guide
119

Across the Alley from the Alamo

Registration 2
Rhythm: Swing

Words and Music by
Joe Greene

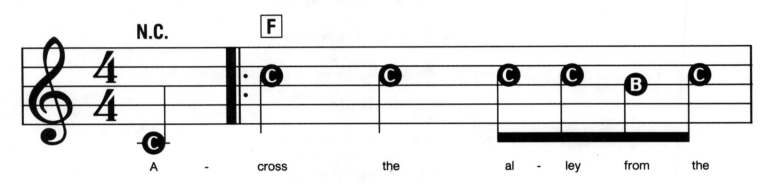

A - cross the al - ley from the

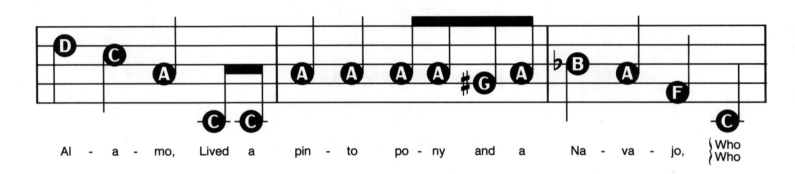

Al - a - mo, Lived a pin - to po - ny and a Na - va - jo, {Who {Who

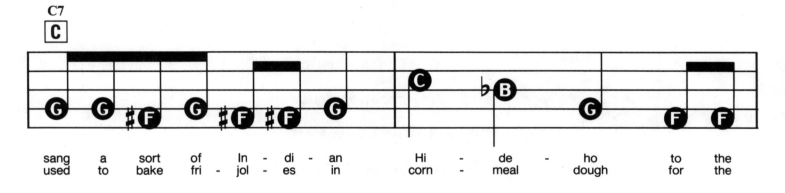

sang a sort of In - di - an Hi - de - ho to the
used to bake fri - jol - es in corn - meal dough for the

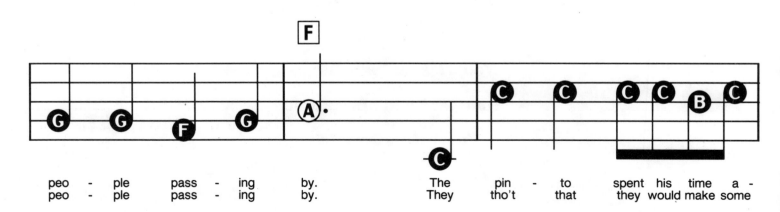

peo - ple pass - ing by. The pin - to spent his time a -
peo - ple pass - ing by. They tho't that they would make some

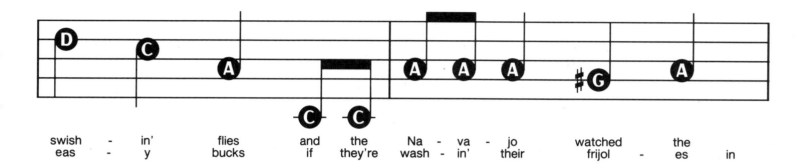

swish - in' flies and the Na - va - jo watched the
eas - y bucks if they're wash - in' their frijol - es in

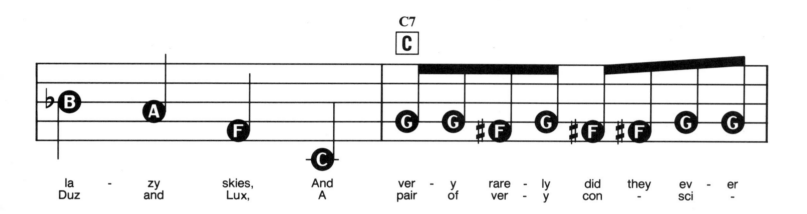

la - zy skies, And ver - y rare - ly did they ev - er
Duz and Lux, A pair of ver - y con - sci -

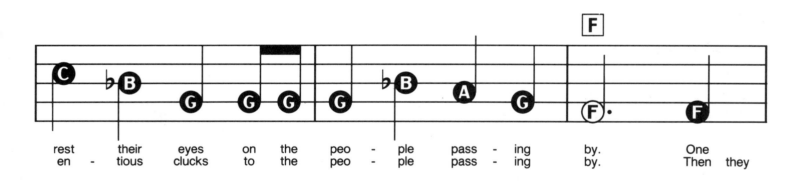

rest their eyes on the peo - ple pass - ing by. One
en - tious clucks to the peo - ple pass - ing by. Then they

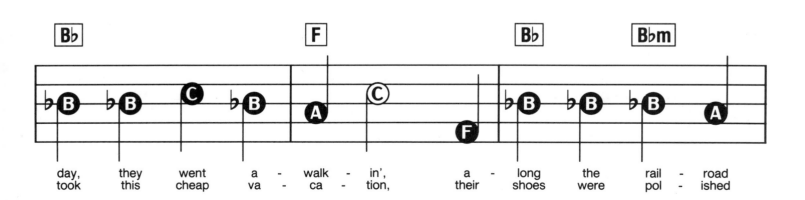

day, they went a - walk - in', a - long the rail - road
took this cheap va - ca - tion, their shoes were pol - ished

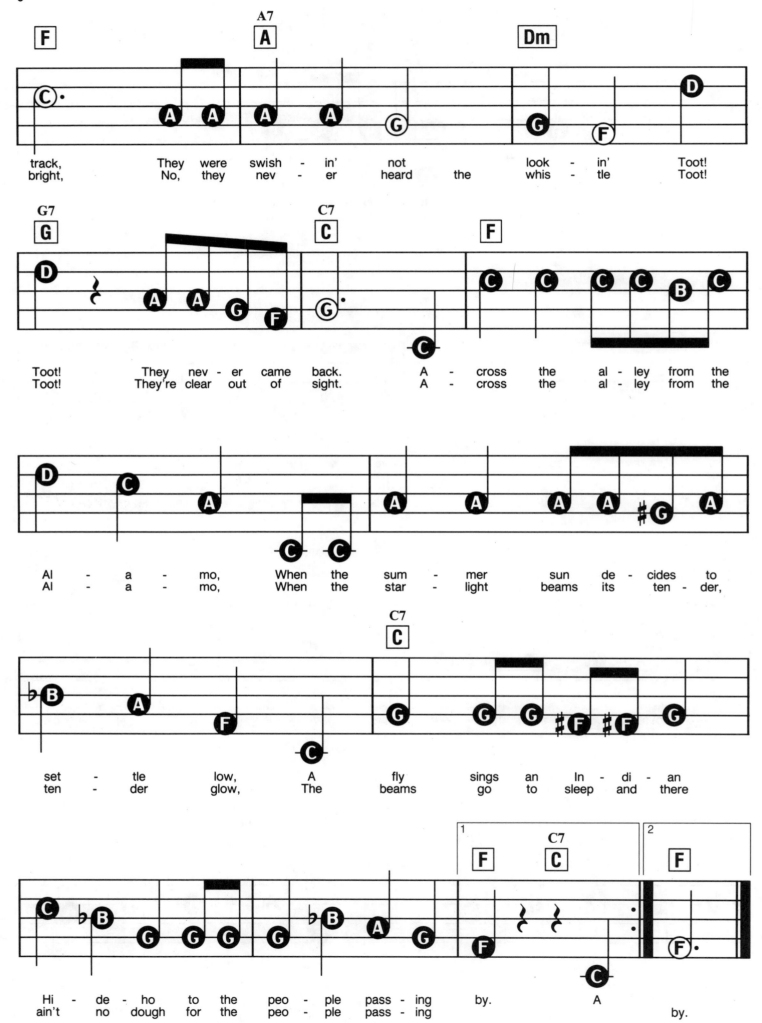

Boogie Woogie Bugle Boy

from BUCK PRIVATES

Registration 7
Rhythm: Shuffle or Fox Trot

Words and Music by
Don Raye and Hughie Prince

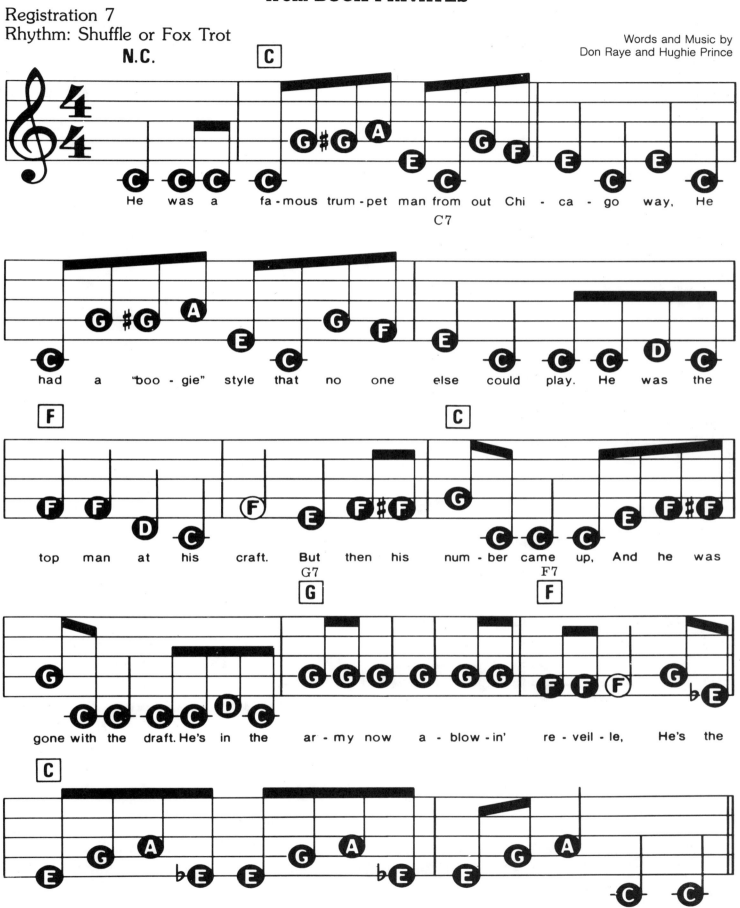

MCA MUSIC PUBLISHING

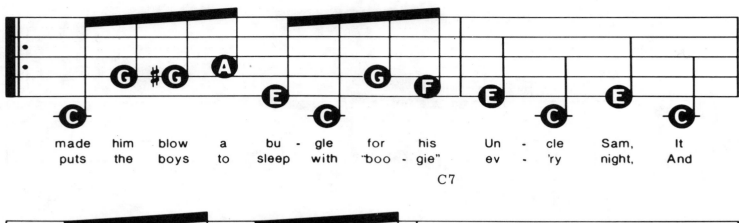

made him blow a bu - gle for his Un - cle Sam, It
puts the boys to sleep with "boo - gie" ev - 'ry night, And

C7

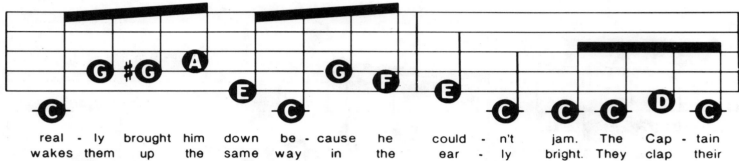

real - ly brought him down be - cause he could - n't jam. The Cap - tain
wakes them up the same way in the ear - ly bright. They clap their

F

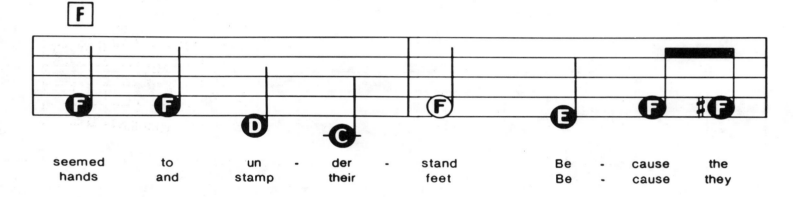

seemed to un - der - stand Be - cause the
hands and stamp their feet Be - cause they

C

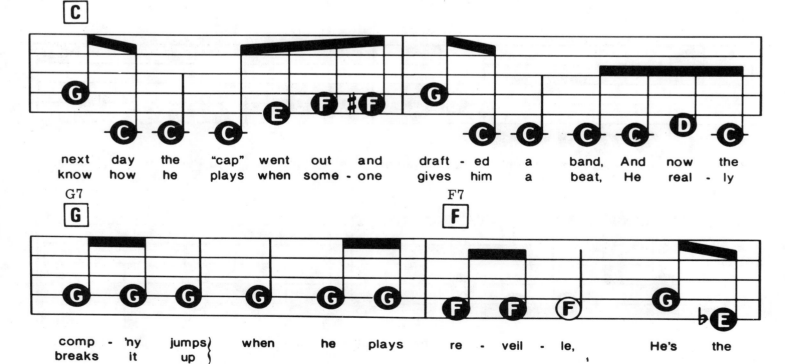

next day the "cap" went out and draft - ed a band, And now the
know how he "cap" plays when some - one gives him a beat, He real - ly

G7

G

F7

F

comp - 'ny jumps} when he plays re - veil - le, He's the
breaks it up }

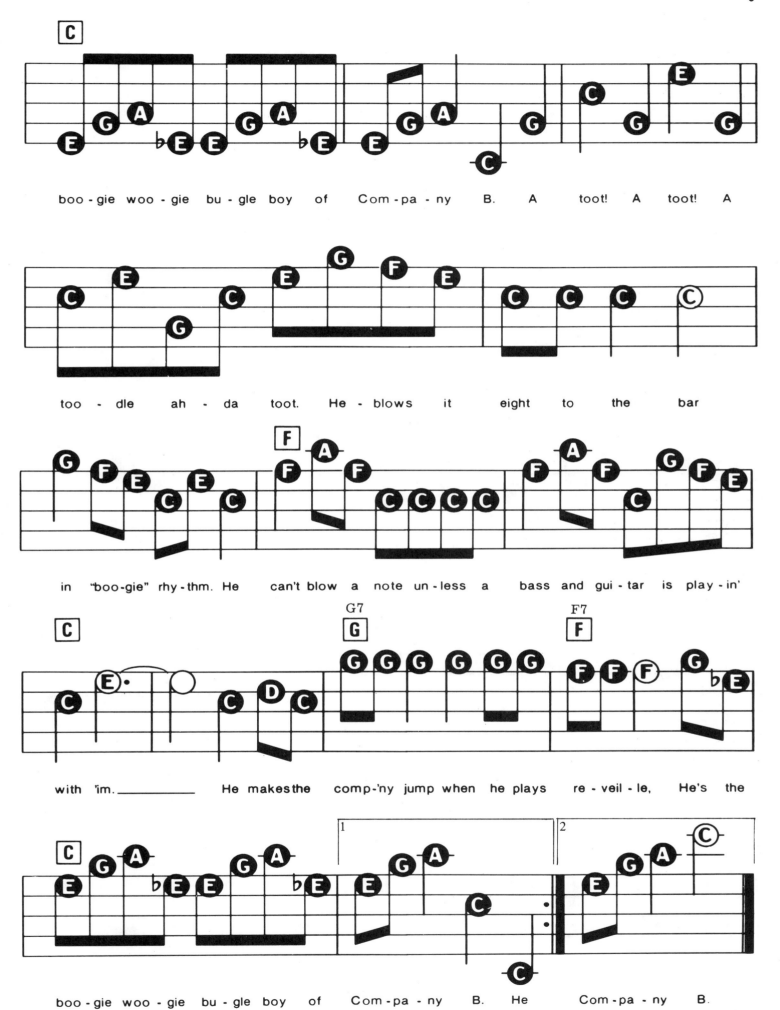

All Through the Day
from CENTENNIAL SUMMER

Registration 3
Rhythm: Swing

Lyrics by Oscar Hammerstein II
Music by Jerome Kern

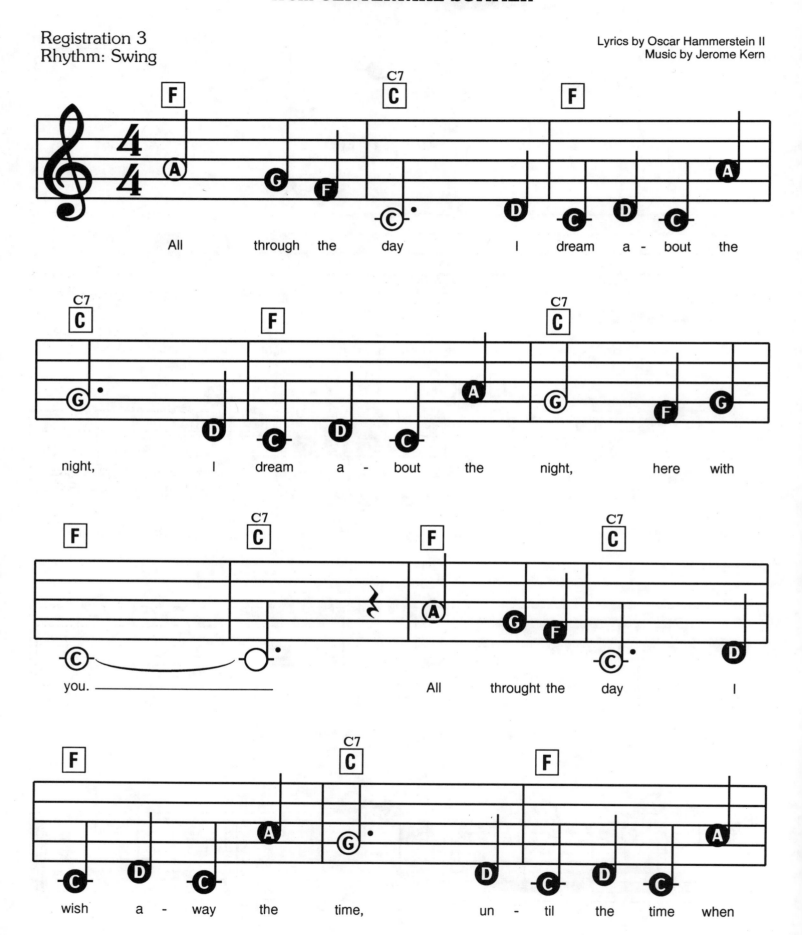

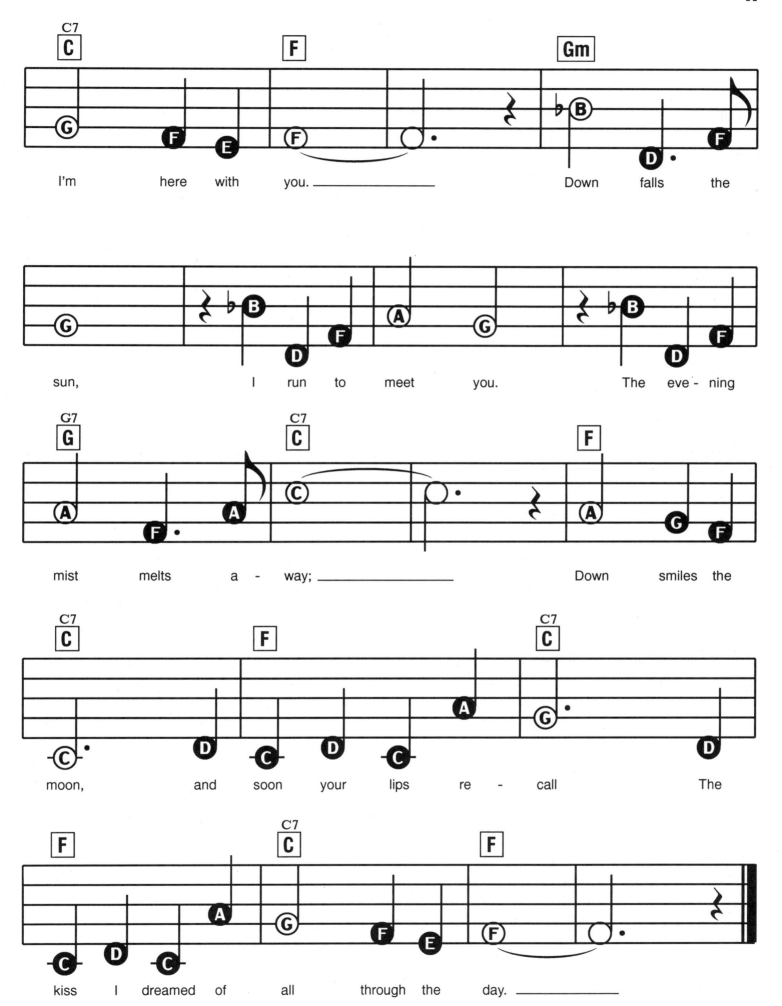

The American Patrol

Registration 4
Rhythm: Fox Trot or Swing

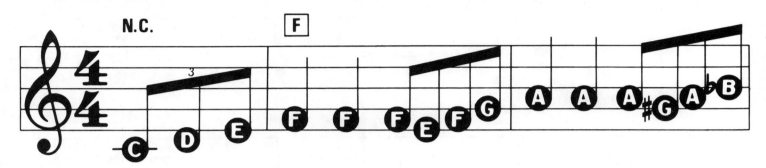

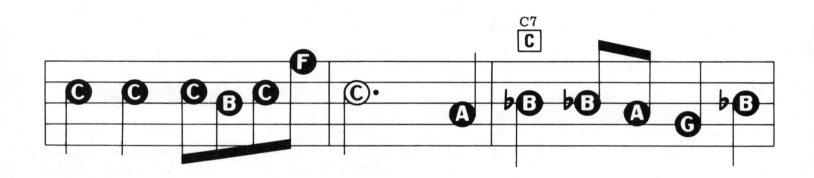

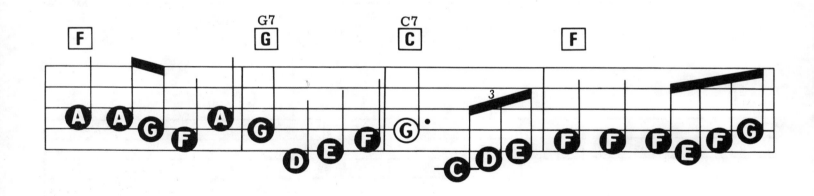

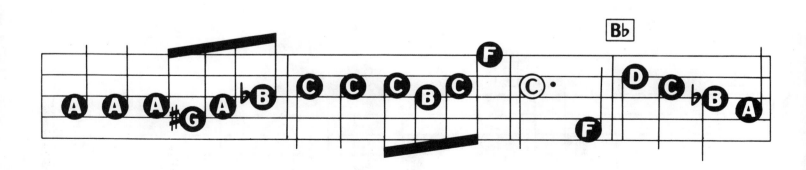

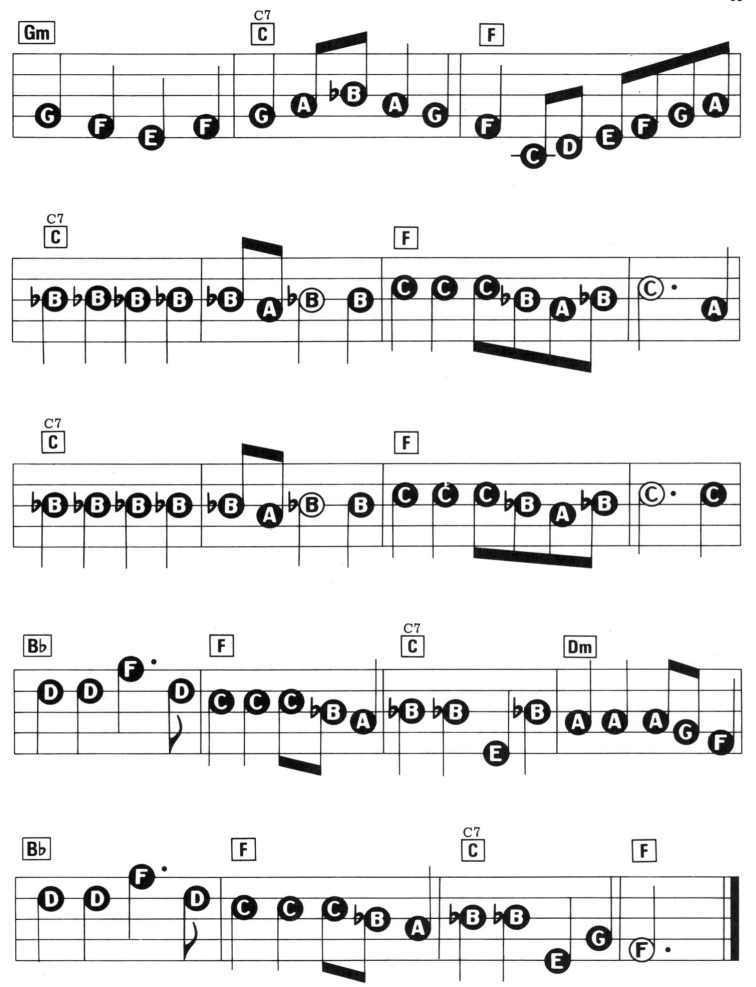

Anniversary Song
from the Columbia Picture THE JOLSON STORY

By Al Jolson and Saul Chaplin

Registration 6
Rhythm: Waltz

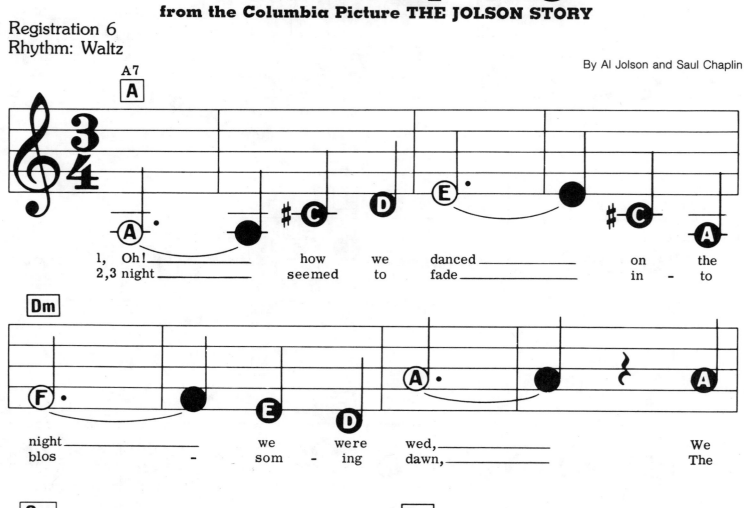

1, Oh!   how   we   danced   on   the
2,3 night   seemed   to   fade   in - to

night   we   were   wed,   We
blos   - som - ing   dawn,   The

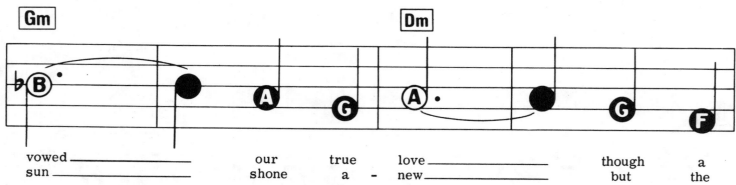

vowed   our   true   love   though   a
sun   shone   a - new   but   the

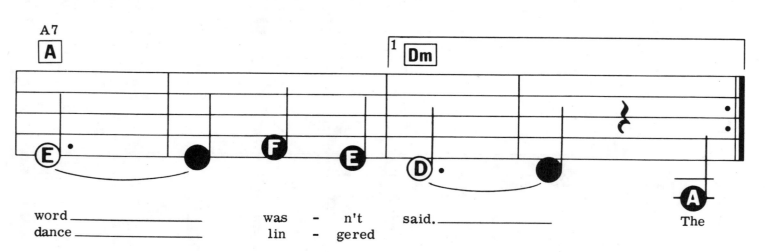

word   was - n't   said.
dance   lin - gered   The

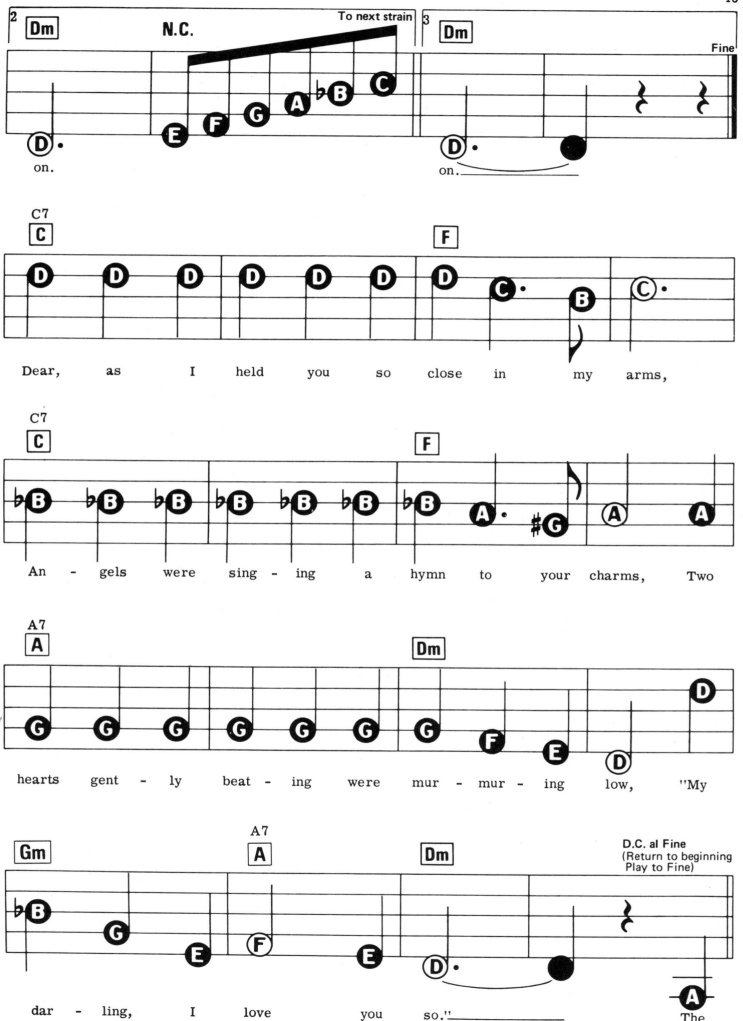

Baby, It's Cold Outside

from the Motion Picture NEPTUNE'S DAUGHTER

Registration 1
Rhythm: Fox Trot or Swing

Words and Music by
Frank Loesser

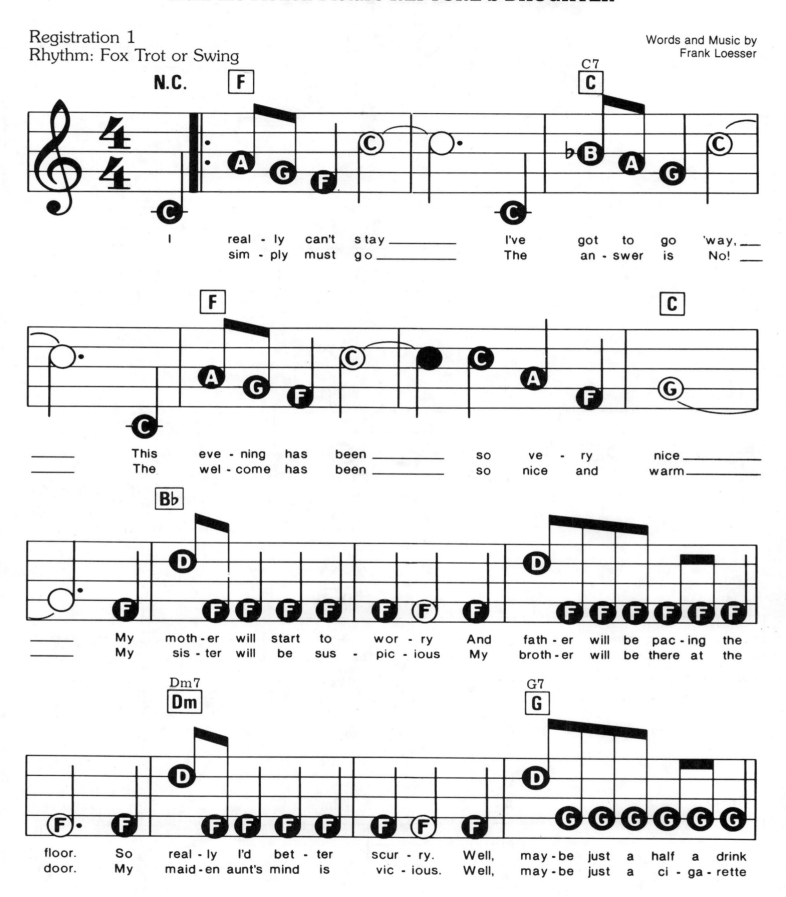

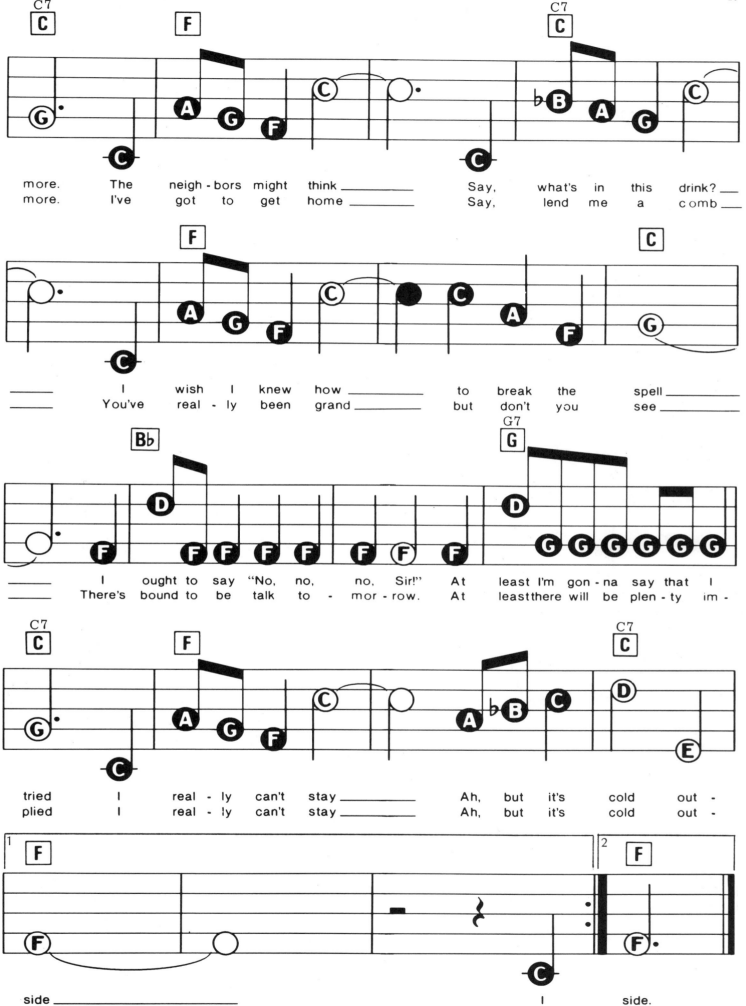

more. The neigh-bors might think _____ Say, what's in this drink?___
more. I've got to get home _____ Say, lend me a comb___

_____ I wish I knew how _____ to break the spell _____
_____ You've real-ly been grand _____ but don't you see _____

_____ I ought to say "No, no, no, Sir!" At least I'm gon-na say that I
_____ There's bound to be talk to-mor-row. At least there will be plen-ty im-

tried I real-ly can't stay _____ Ah, but it's cold out-
plied I real-ly can't stay _____ Ah, but it's cold out-

side _____   I side.

Bali Ha'i
from SOUTH PACIFIC

Registration 3
Rhythm: Fox Trot

Lyrics by Oscar Hammerstein II
Music by Richard Rodgers

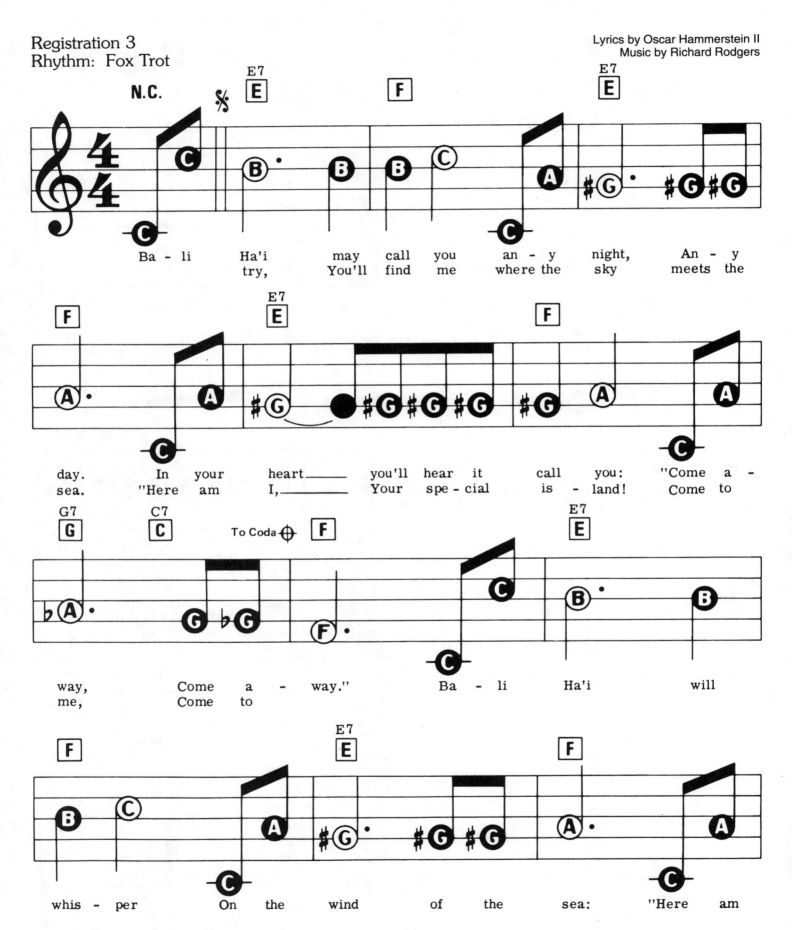

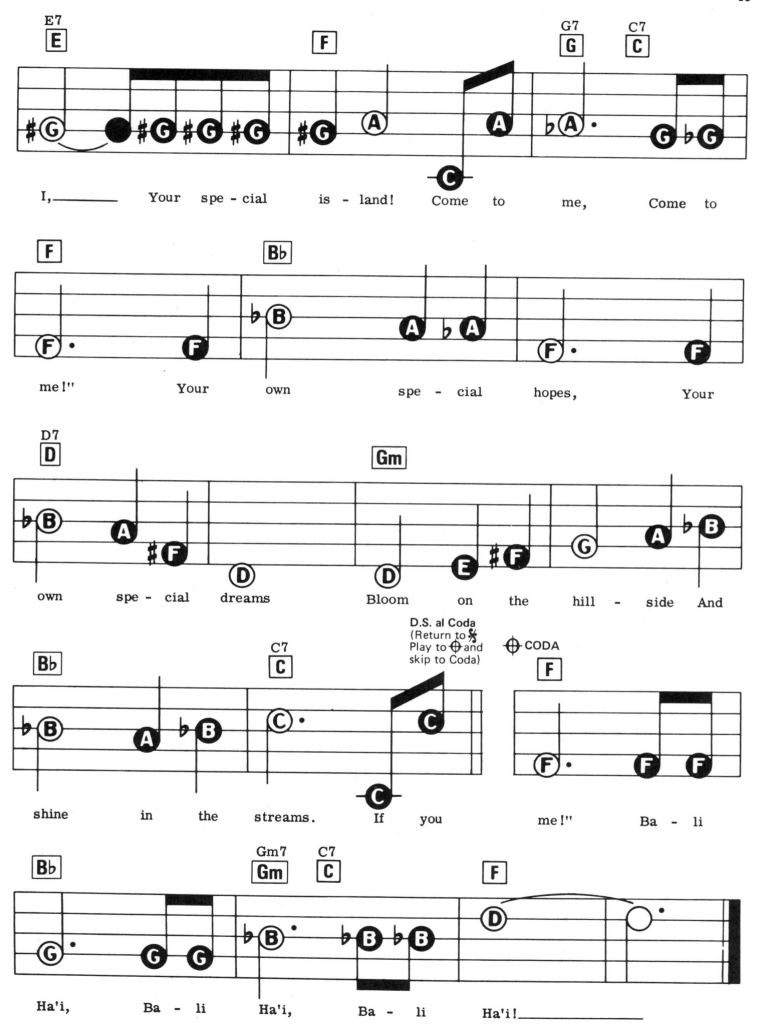

Beat Me Daddy, Eight to the Bar

Registration 4
Rhythm: Shuffle or Swing

Words and Music by Don Raye,
Hughie Prince and Eleanor Sheehy

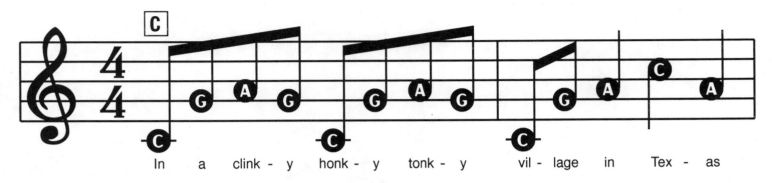

In a clink-y honk-y tonk-y vil-lage in Tex-as

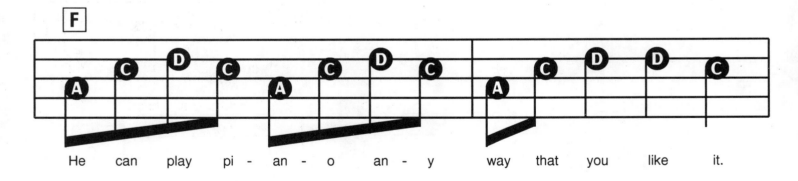

there's a guy who plays the best pi-an-o by far.

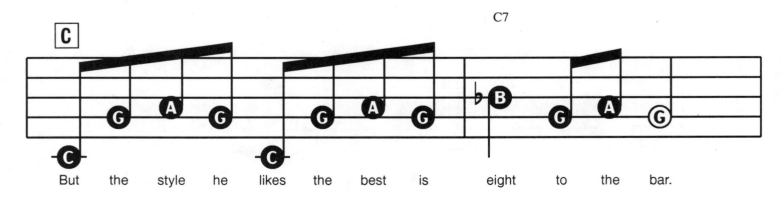

He can play pi-an-o an-y way that you like it.

But the style he likes the best is eight to the bar.

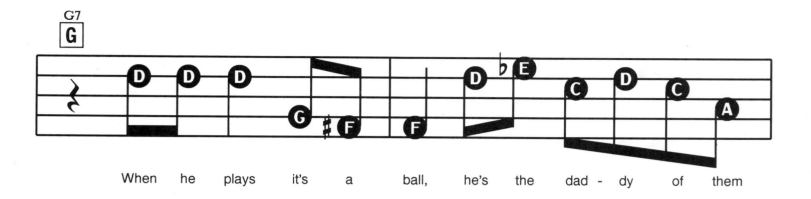

When he plays it's a ball, he's the dad - dy of them

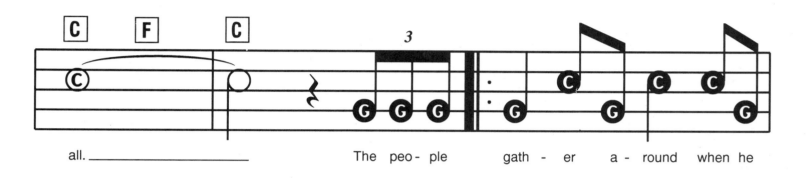

all. _____ The peo - ple gath - er a - round when he

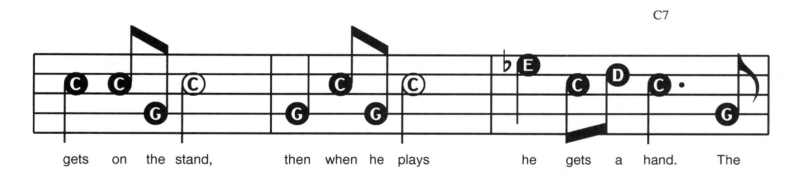

gets on the stand, then when he plays he gets a hand. The

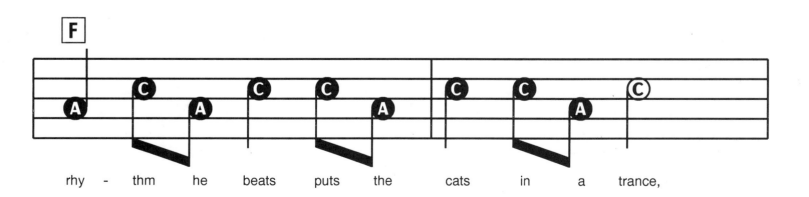

rhy - thm he beats puts the cats in a trance,

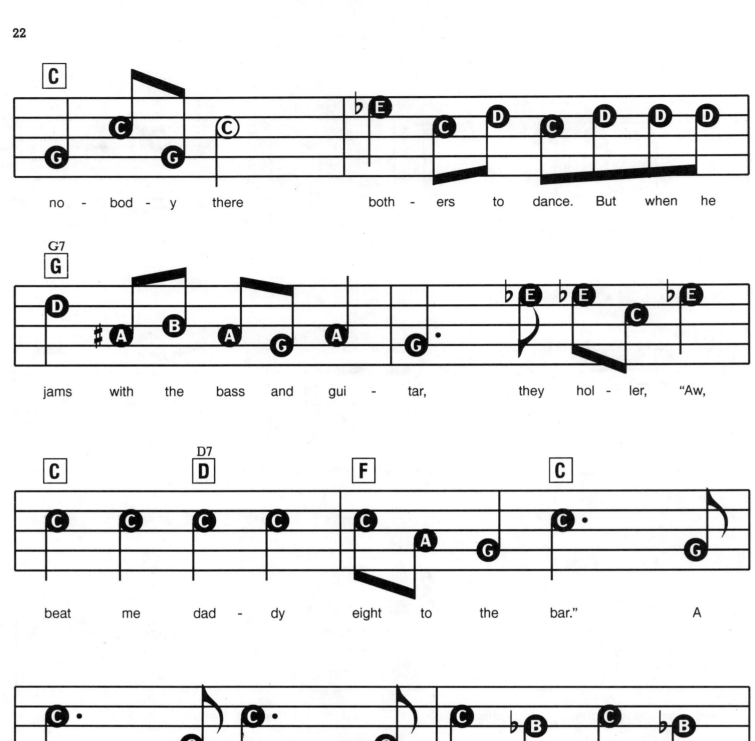

no - bod - y there   both - ers to dance. But when he

jams with the bass and gui - tar,   they hol - ler, "Aw,

beat me dad - dy   eight to the bar."   A

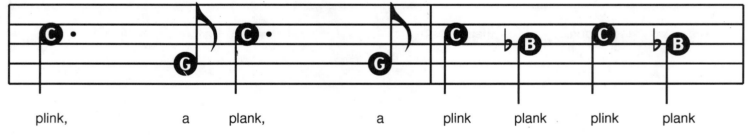

plink,   a plank,   a plink plank plink plank

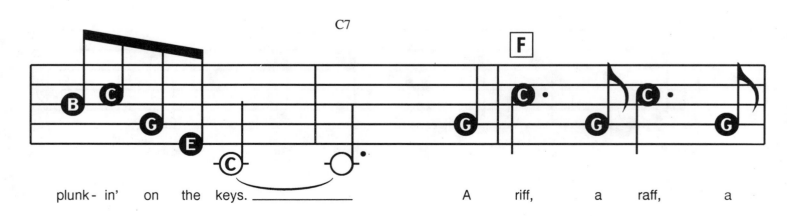

plunk - in' on the keys. _____ A riff, a raff, a

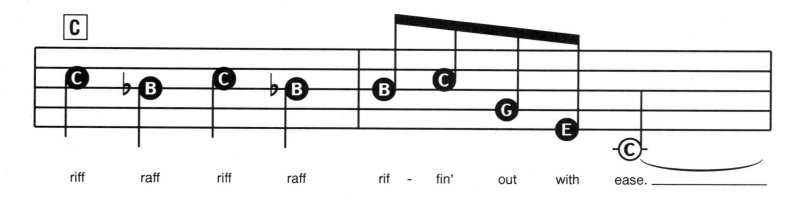

riff raff riff raff rif - fin' out with ease. _____

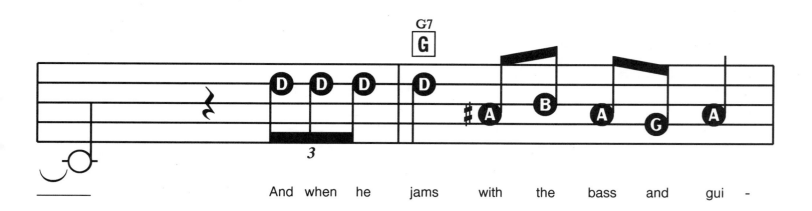

____ And when he jams with the bass and gui -

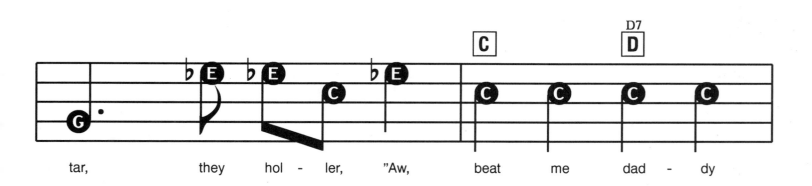

tar, they hol - ler, "Aw, beat me dad - dy

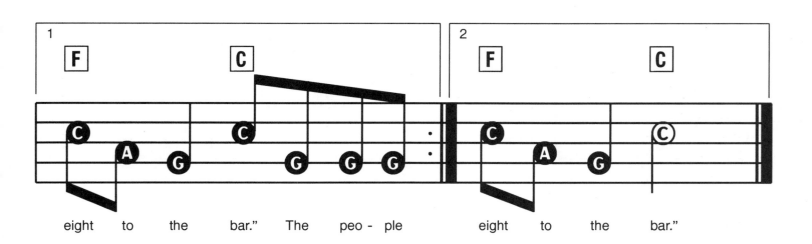

eight to the bar." The peo - ple   eight to the bar."

Bésame Mucho
(Kiss Me Much)

Registration 5
Rhythm: Latin or Rhumba

English Lyric by Sunny Skylar
Music and Spanish Lyric by Consuelo Velazquez

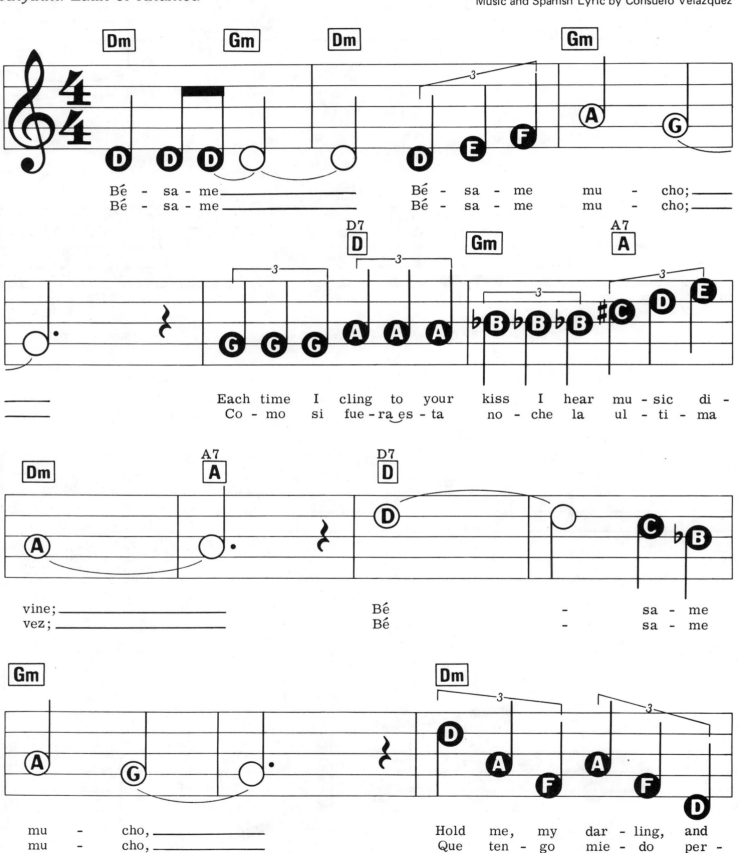

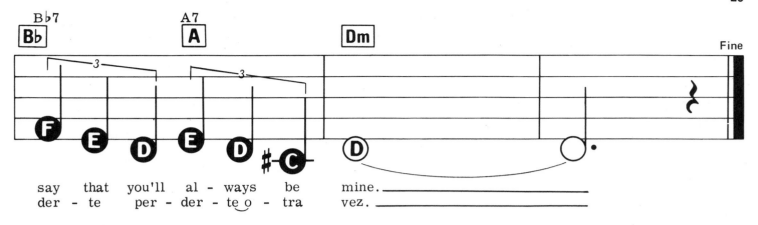

say that you'll al - ways be mine. _____
der - te per - der - te o - tra vez. _____

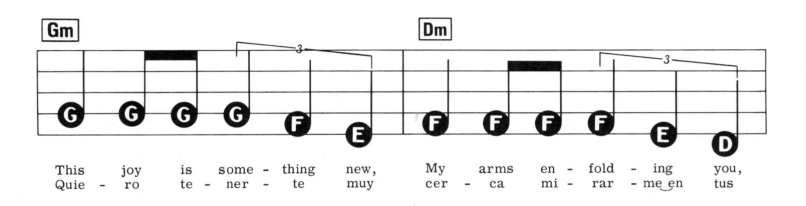

This joy is some - thing new, My arms en - fold - ing you,
Quie - ro te - ner - te muy cer - ca mi - rar - me en tus

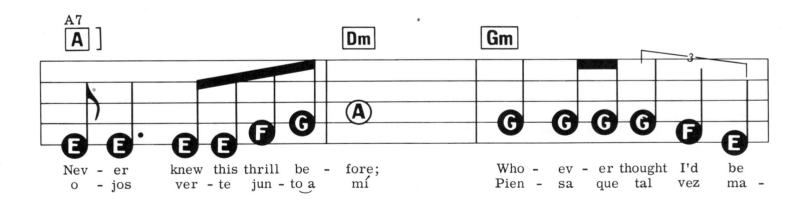

Nev - er knew this thrill be - fore; Who - ev - er thought I'd be
o - jos ver - te jun - to a mí Pien - sa que tal vez ma -

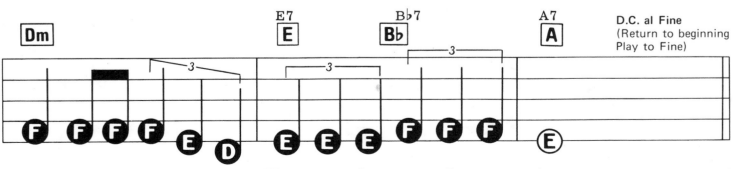

hold - ing you close to me, Whisp-'ring "It's you I a - dore;"
ña - na yo ya es - ta - ré le - jos muy le - jos de ti.

Bibbidi-Bobbidi-Boo
(The Magic Song)
from Walt Disney's CINDERELLA

Registration 8
Rhythm: Swing

Words by Jerry Livingston
Music by Mack David and Al Hoffman

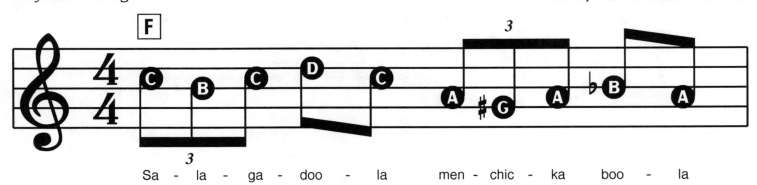

Sa - la - ga - doo - la men - chic - ka boo - la

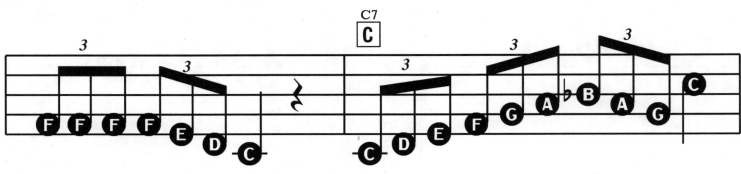

bib - bi - di - bob - bi - di - boo   Put 'em to - geth - er and what have you got

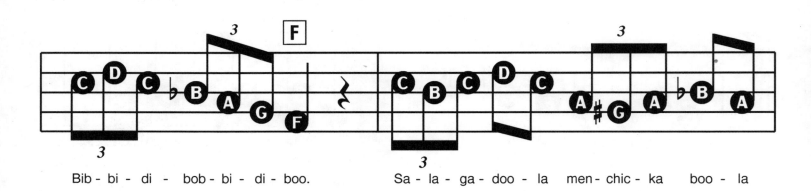

Bib - bi - di - bob - bi - di - boo.   Sa - la - ga - doo - la men - chic - ka boo - la

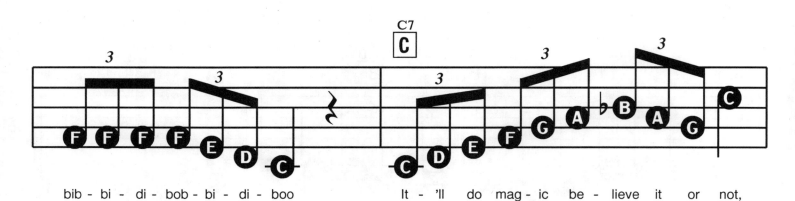

bib - bi - di - bob - bi - di - boo   It - 'll do mag - ic be - lieve it or not,

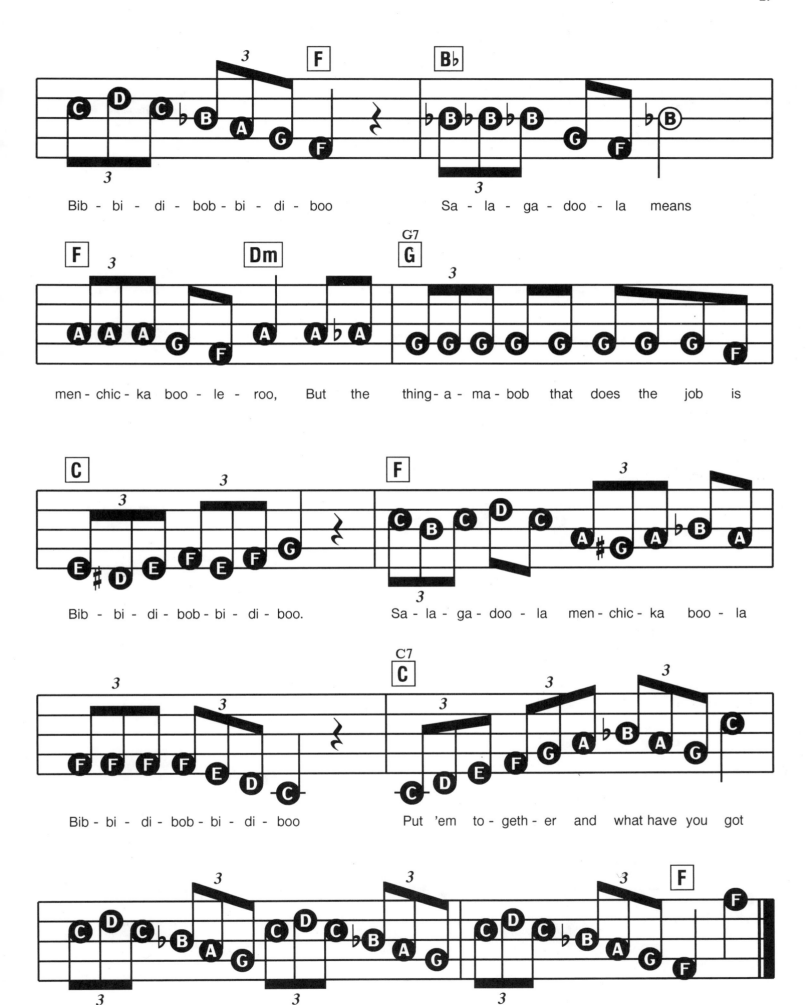

Blue Champagne

Registration 3
Rhythm: Ballad or Slow Rock

Words and Music by Grady Watts,
Frank Ryerson & Jimmy Eaton

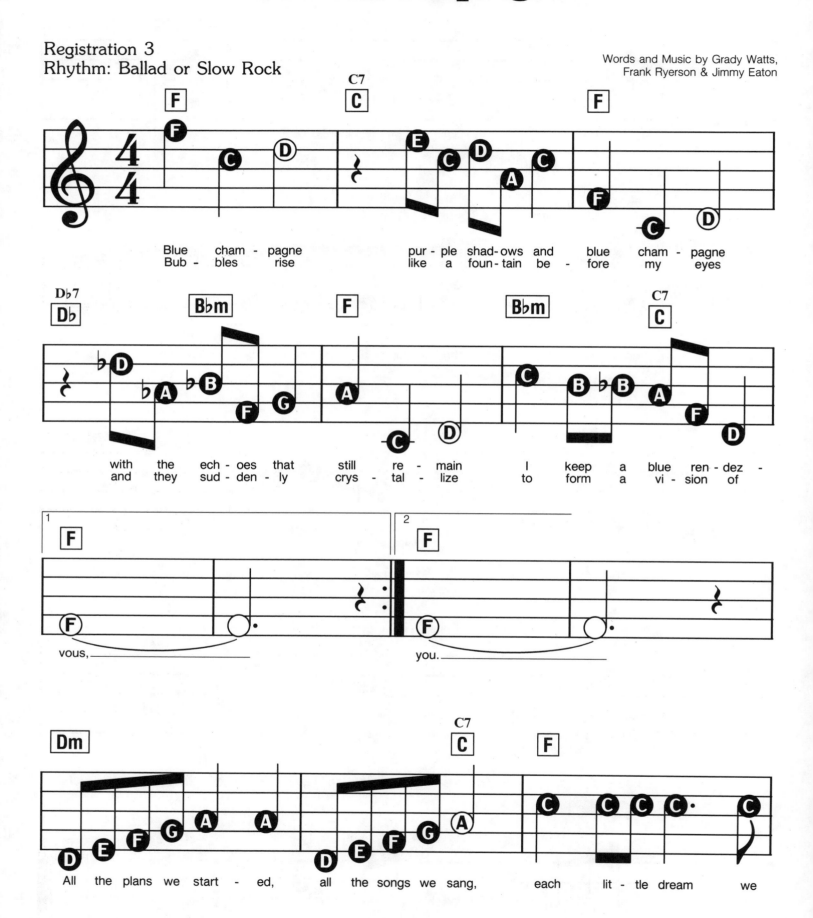

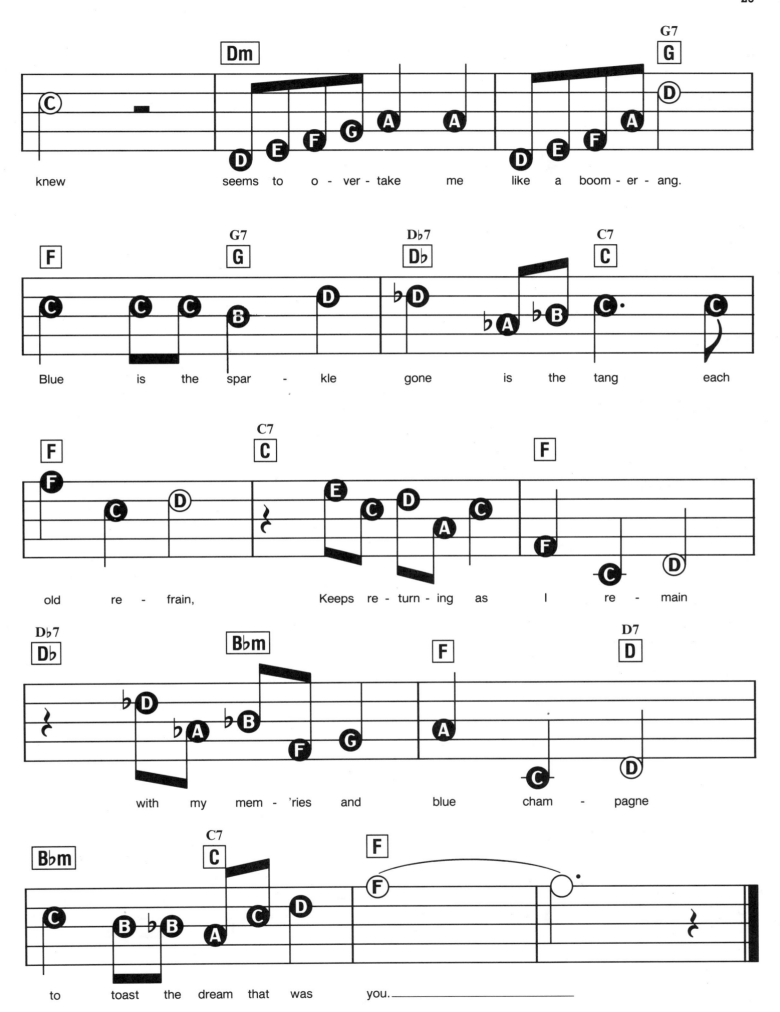

Bye Bye Baby
from GENTLEMEN PREFER BLONDES

Registration 9
Rhythm: Fox Trot or Swing

Lyrics by Leo Robin
Music by Jule Styne

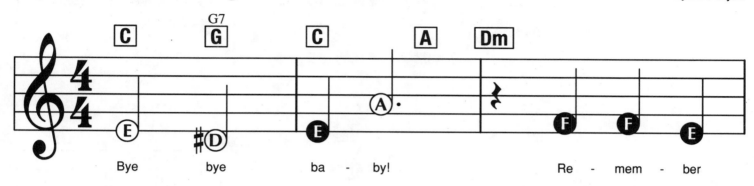

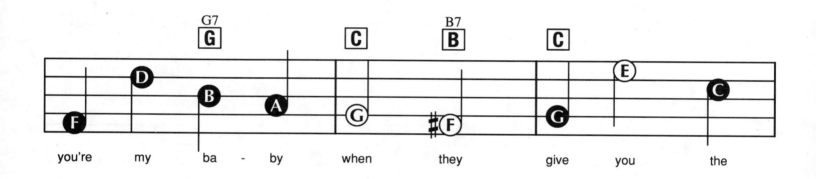

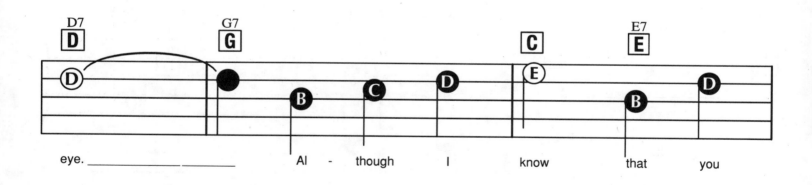

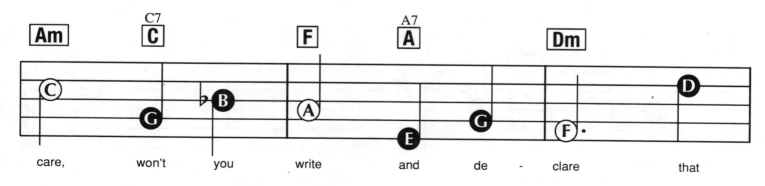

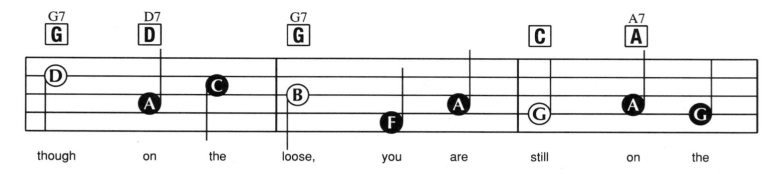

though   on   the   loose,   you   are   still   on   the

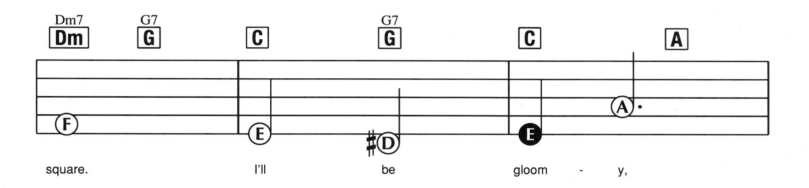

square.   I'll   be   gloom - y,

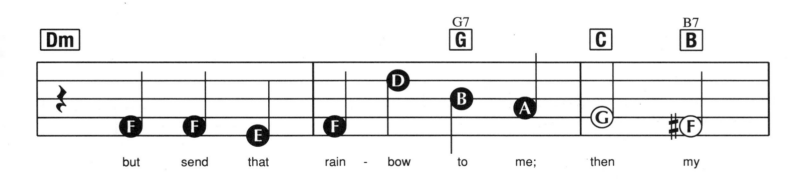

but   send   that   rain - bow   to   me;   then   my

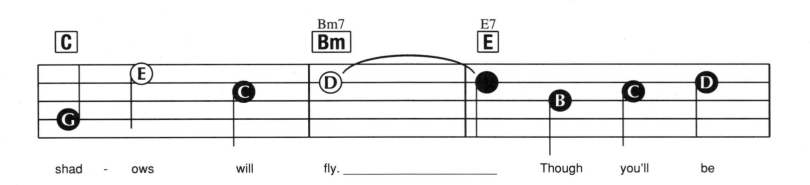

shad - ows   will   fly. _____   Though   you'll   be

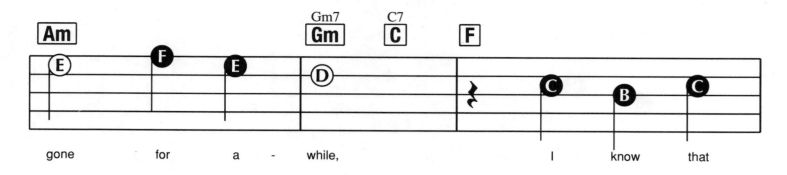

gone   for   a - while,   I   know   that

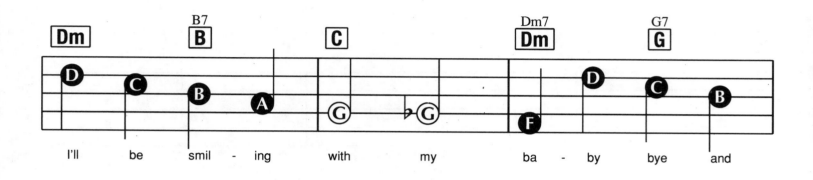

I'll   be   smil - ing   with   my   ba - by   bye   and

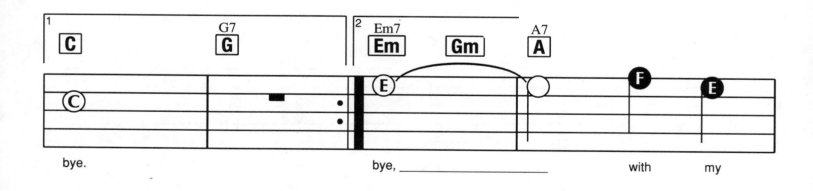

bye.   bye, _____   with   my

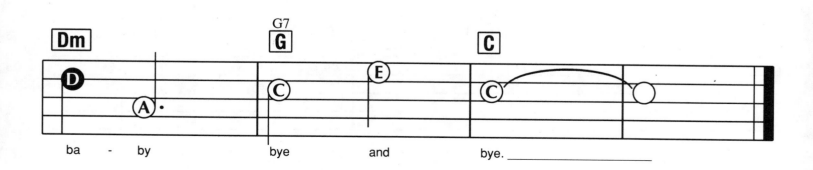

ba - by   bye   and   bye. _____

Cruising Down the River

Registration 9
Rhythm: Waltz

Words and Music by
Eily Beadell and Nell Tollerton

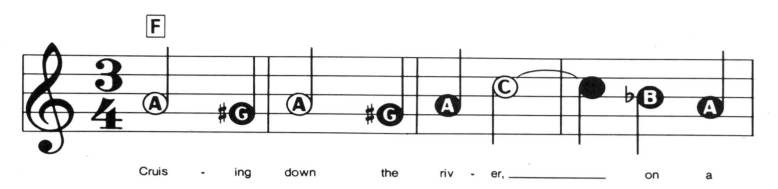

Cruis - ing down the riv - er, _____ on a

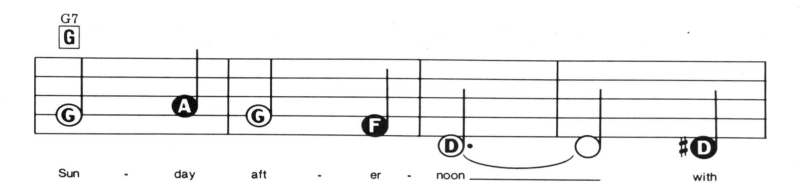

Sun - day aft - er - noon _____ with

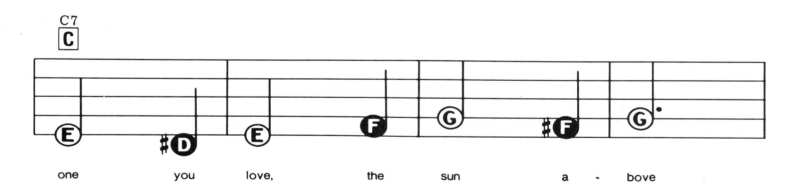

one you love, the sun a - bove

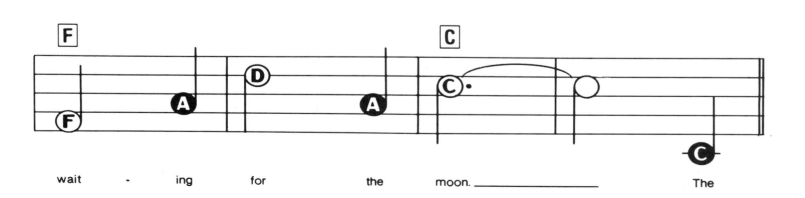

wait - ing for the moon. _____ The

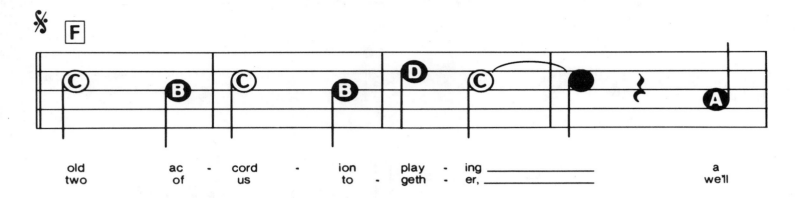

old   ac - cord - ion   play - ing _____   a
two   of   us   to - geth - er, _____ we'll

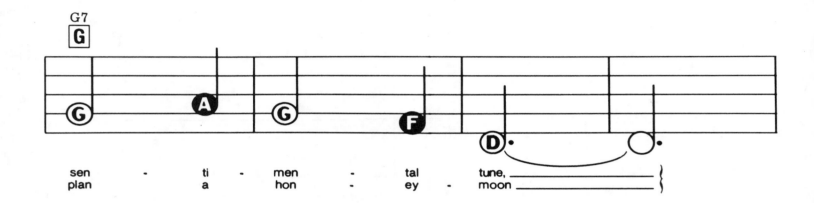

sen -   ti - men -   tal   tune, _____
plan   a   hon -   ey - moon _____

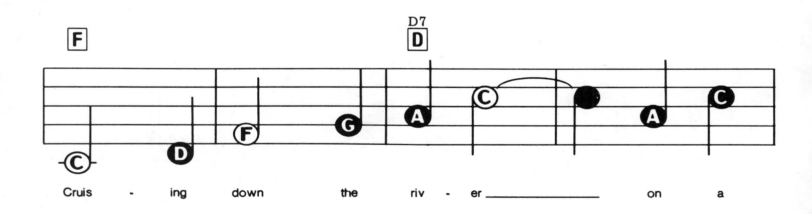

Cruis - ing   down   the   riv - er _____ on a

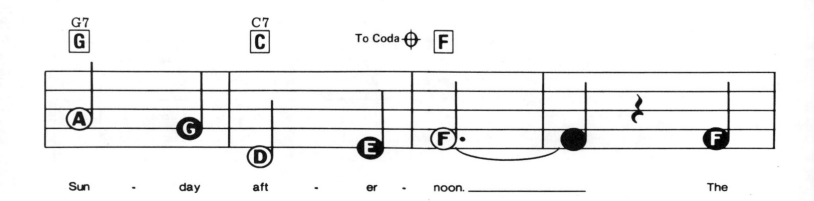

Sun - day   aft - er - noon. _____   The

F7

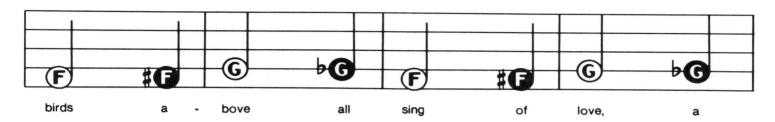

birds   a - bove   all   sing   of   love,   a

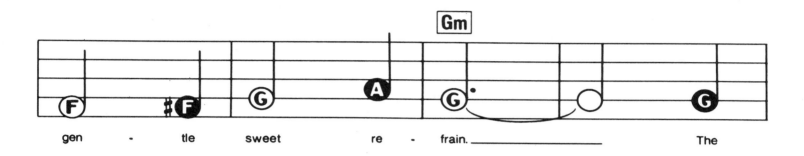

gen - tle   sweet   re - frain. _____   The

G7

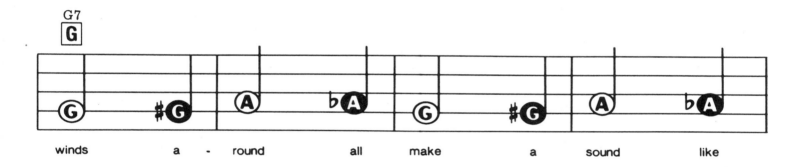

winds   a - round   all   make   a   sound   like

C7

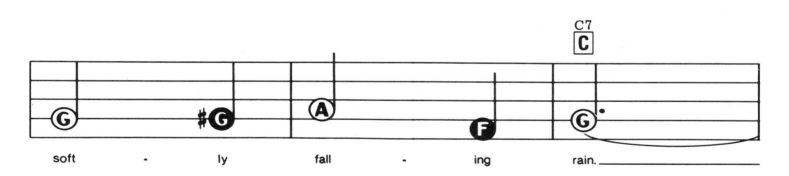

soft - ly   fall - ing   rain. _____

D.S. al Coda
(Return to %
Play to ⊕ and
skip to Coda)

CODA
⊕

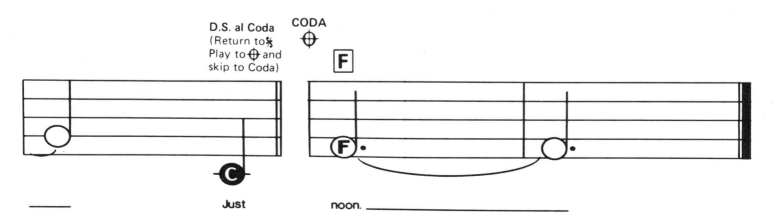

_____   Just   noon. _____

Chiquita Banana

Registration 8
Rhythm: Cha-Cha

Words and Music by Len Mackenzie,
Garth Montgomery and William Wirges

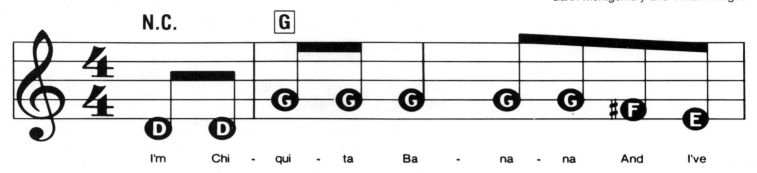

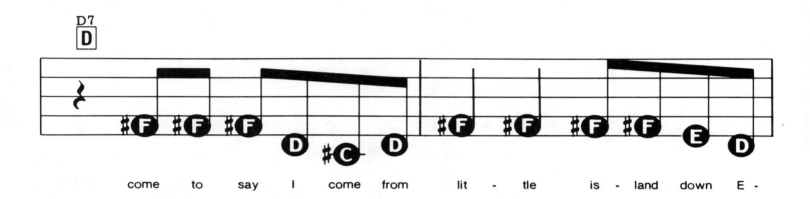

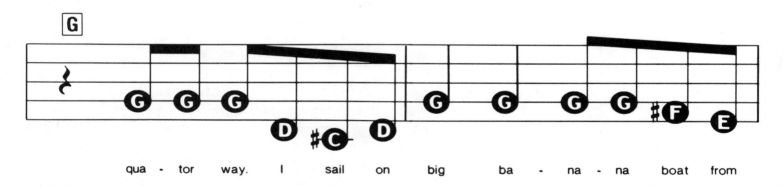

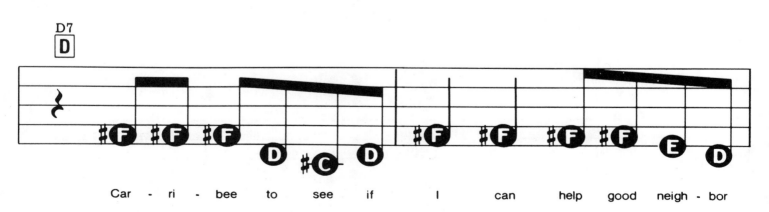

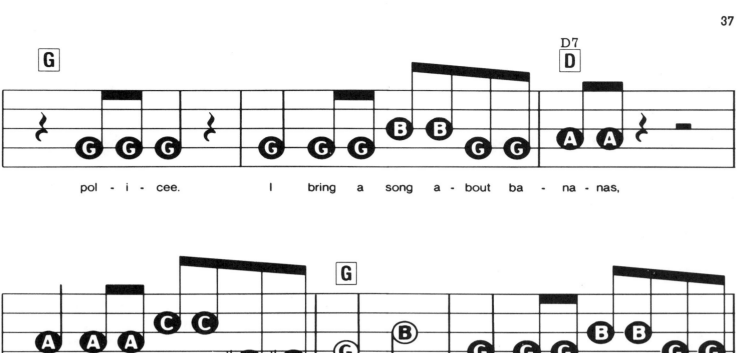

pol - i - cee.　　I　bring　a　song　a - bout　ba - na - nas,

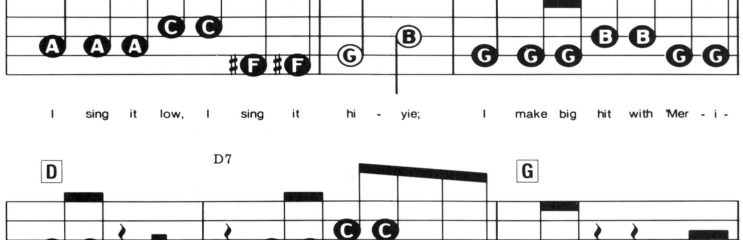

I　sing　it　low,　I　sing　it　hi - yie;　　I　make　big　hit　with　'Mer - i -

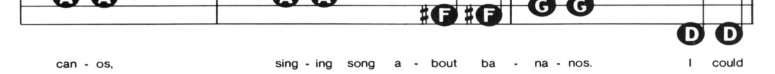

can - os,　　　sing - ing　song　a - bout　ba - na - nos.　　　　　I　could

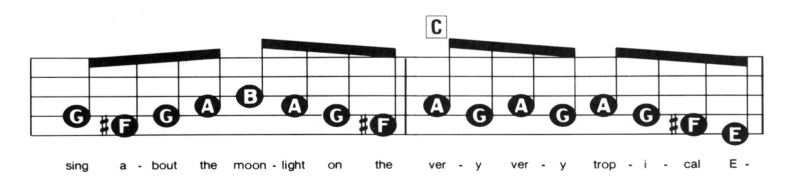

sing　a - bout　the　moon - light　on　the　ver - y　ver - y　trop - i - cal　E -

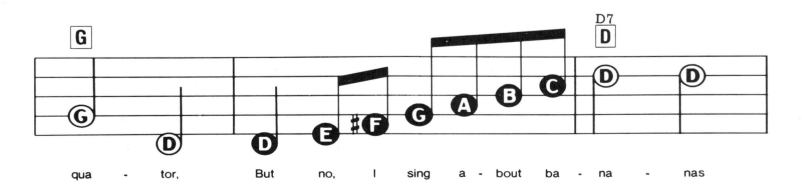

qua - tor,　　But　no,　I　sing　a - bout　ba - na - nas

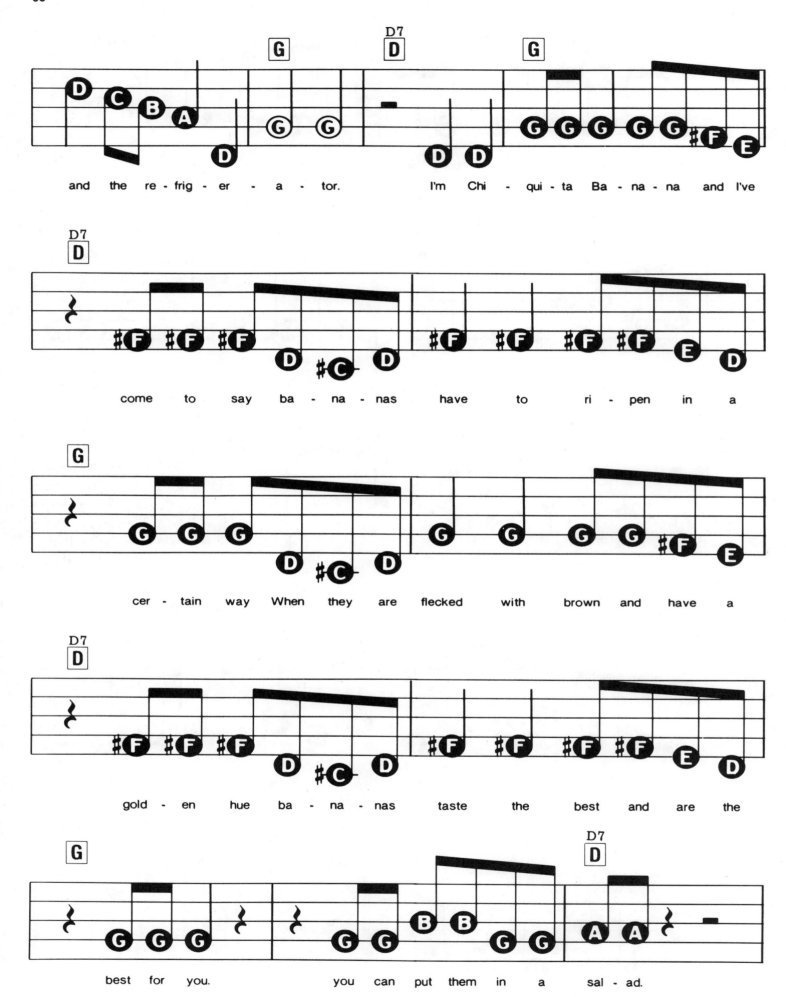

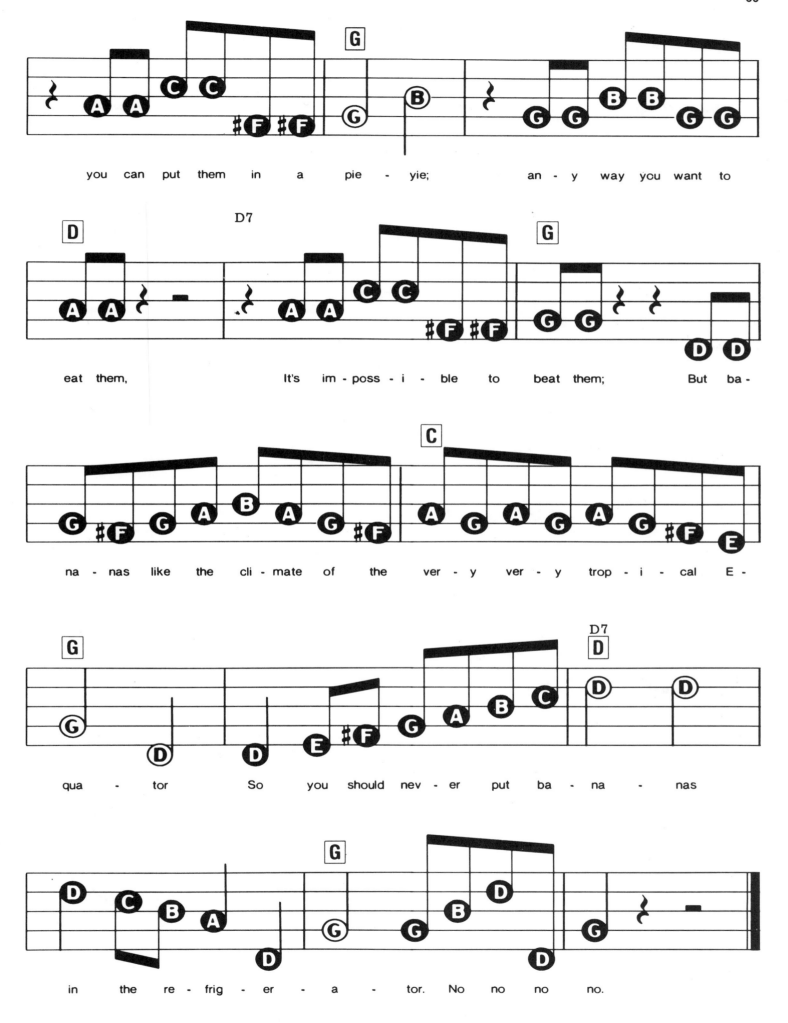

Day by Day
Theme from the Paramount Television Series DAY BY DAY

Registration 4
Rhythm: Swing

Words and Music by Sammy Cahn,
Axel Stordahl and Paul Weston

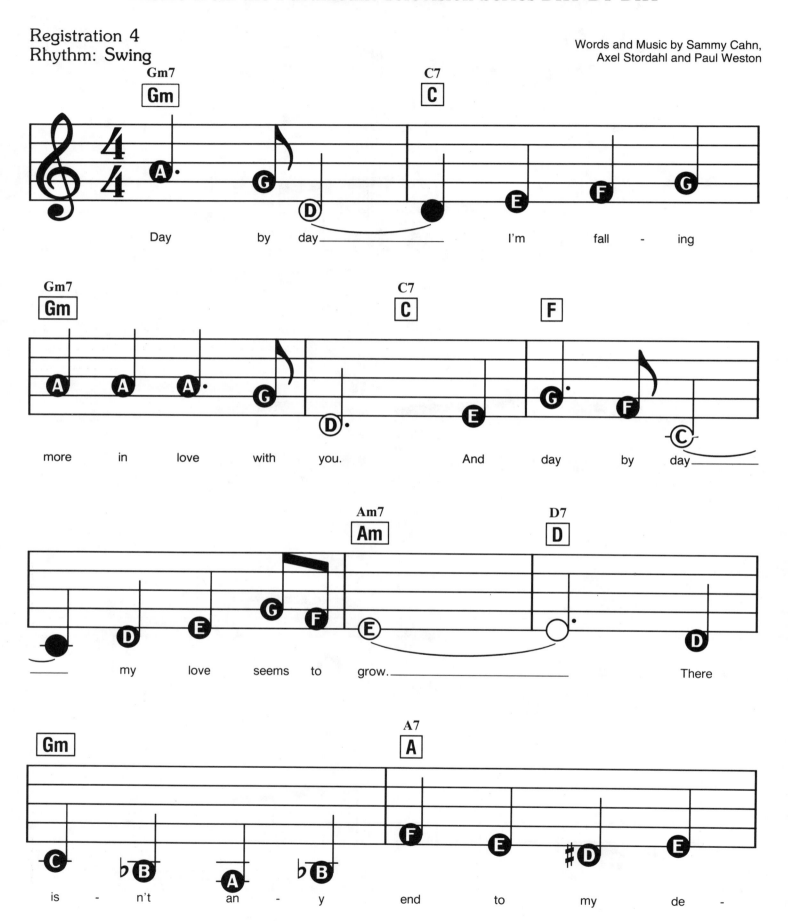

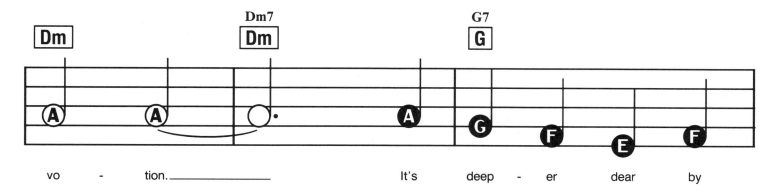

vo - tion._____ It's deep - er dear by

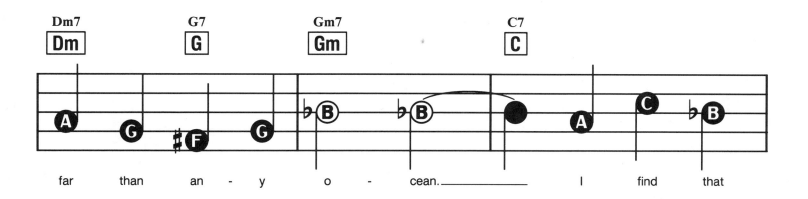

far than an - y o - cean._____ I find that

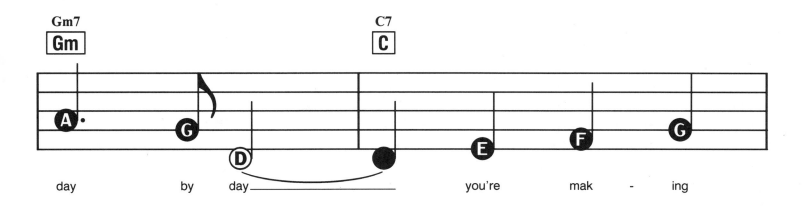

day by day_____ you're mak - ing

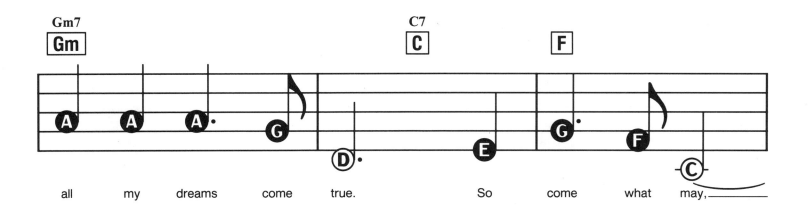

all my dreams come true. So come what may,_____

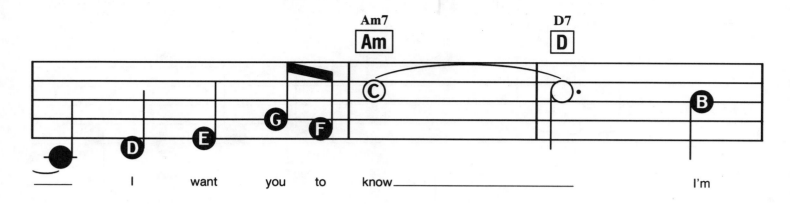

I want you to know I'm

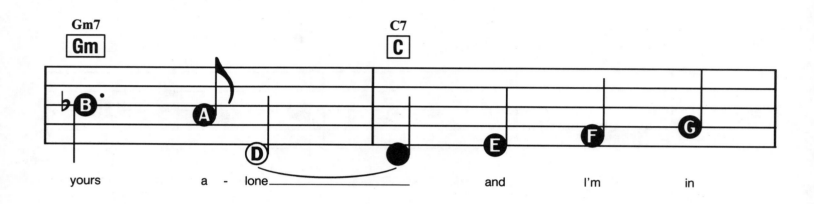

yours a - lone and I'm in

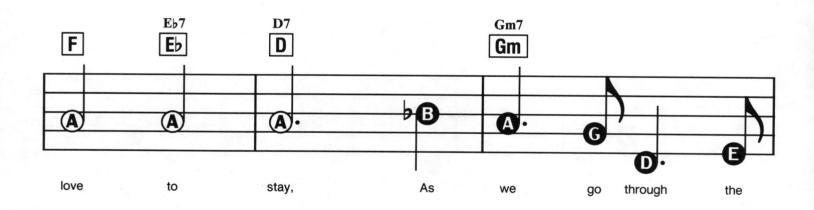

love to stay, As we go through the

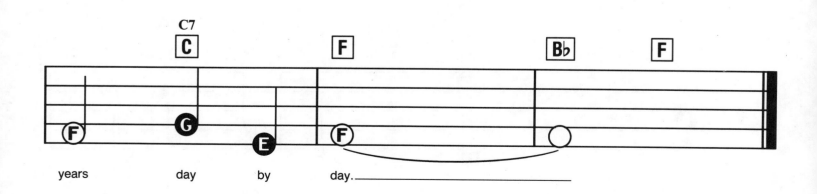

years day by day.

Don't Get Around Much Anymore

Registration 7
Rhythm: Swing

Words and Music by Bob Russell
and Duke Ellington

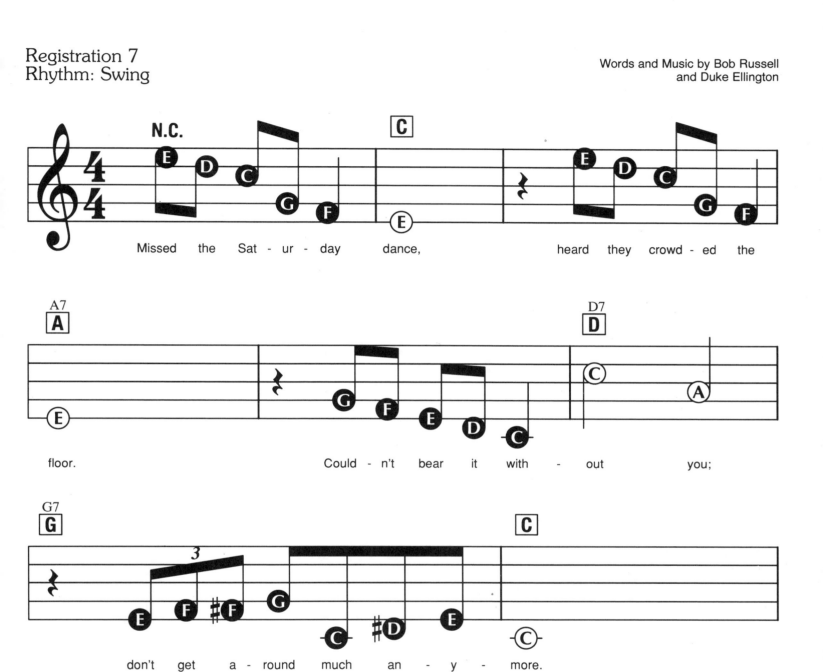

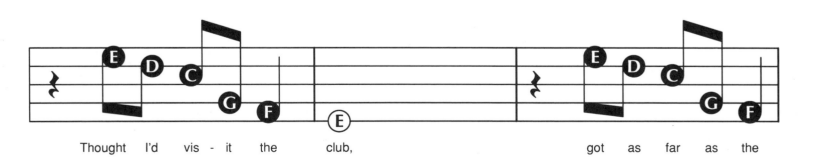

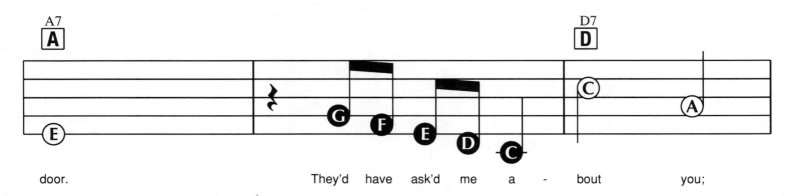

door.   They'd   have   ask'd   me   a - bout   you;

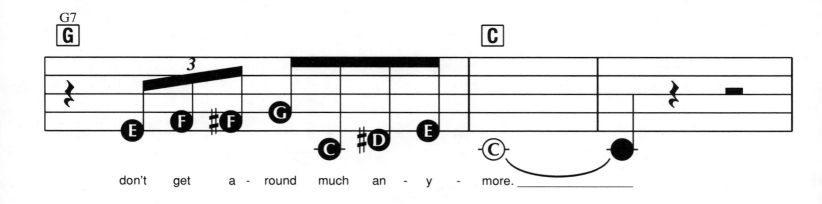

don't   get   a - round   much   an - y - more. _____

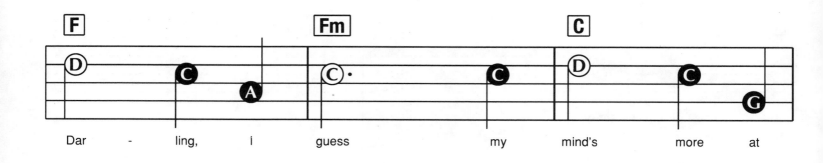

Dar - ling,   I   guess   my   mind's   more   at

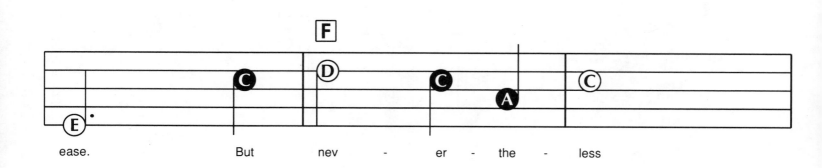

ease.   But   nev - er - the - less

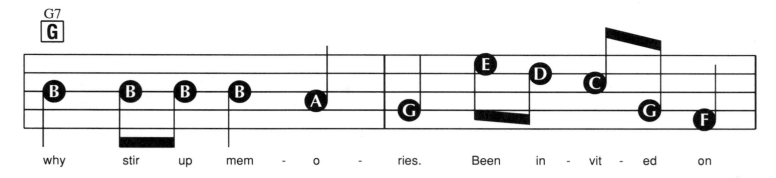

why stir up mem - o - ries. Been in - vit - ed on

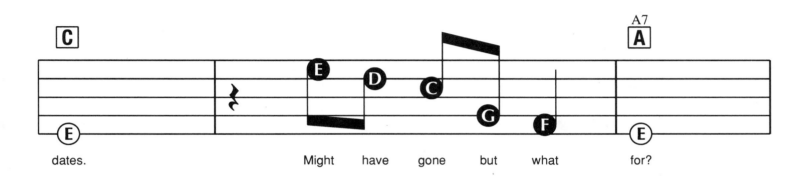

dates. Might have gone but what for?

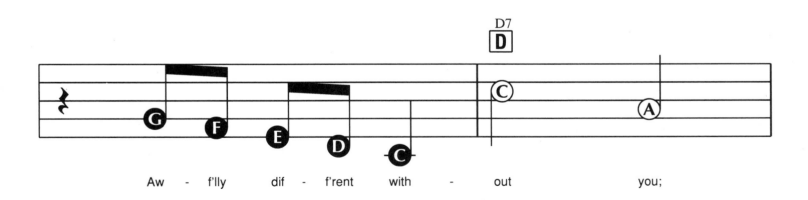

Aw - f'lly dif - f'rent with - out you;

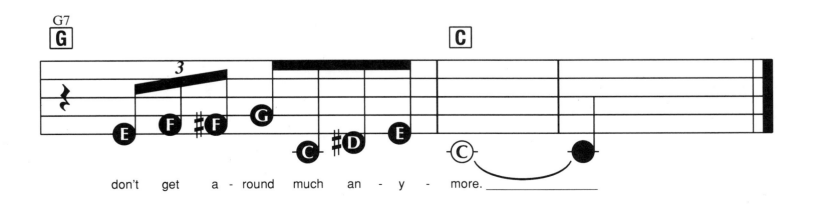

don't get a - round much an - y - more. _____

Diamonds Are a Girl's Best Friend
from GENTLEMEN PREFER BLONDES

Registration 5
Rhythm: March or Polka

Lyrics by Leo Robin
Music by Jule Styne

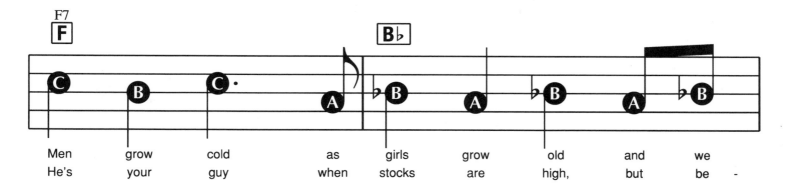

Men grow cold as girls grow old and we
He's your guy when stocks are high, but be -

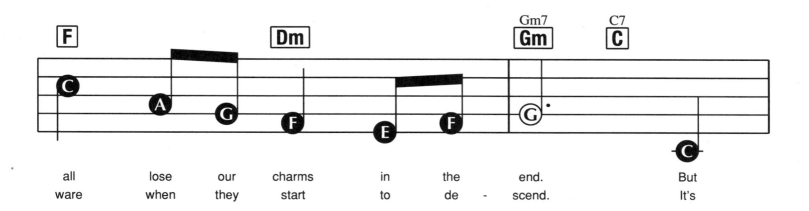

all lose our charms in the end. But
ware when they start to de - scend. It's

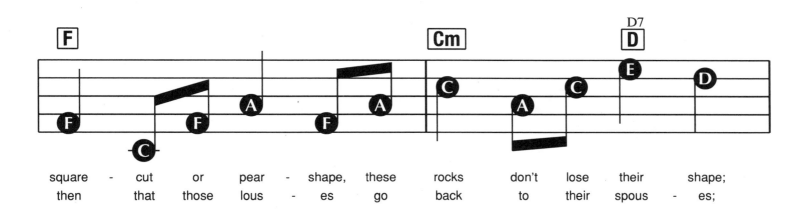

square - cut or pear - shape, these rocks don't lose their shape;
then that those lous - es go rocks back to their spous - es;

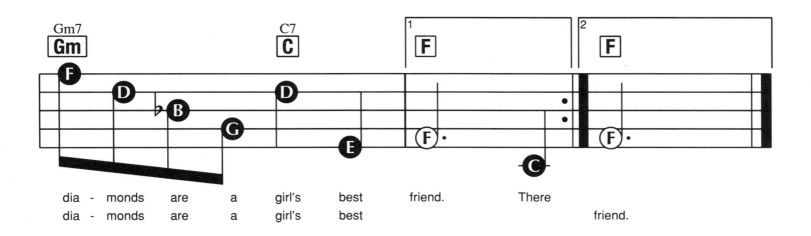

dia - monds are a girl's best friend. There
dia - monds are a girl's best friend.

A Dream Is a Wish
Your Heart Makes
from Walt Disney's CINDERELLA

Registration 1
Rhythm: Ballad or Fox Trot

Words and Music by Mack David,
Al Hoffman and Jerry Livingston

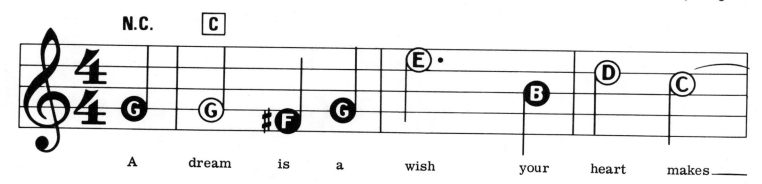

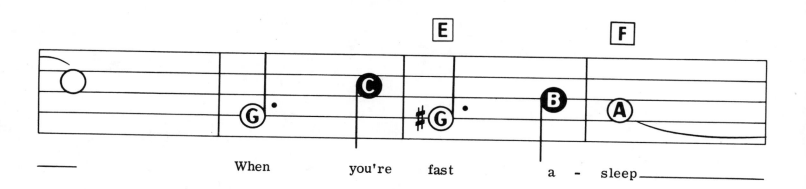

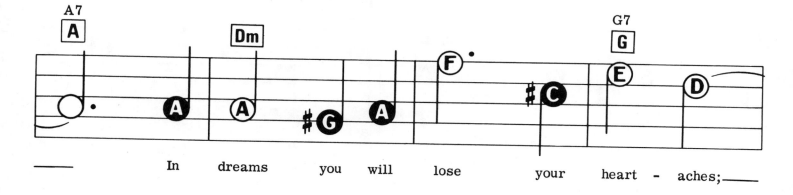

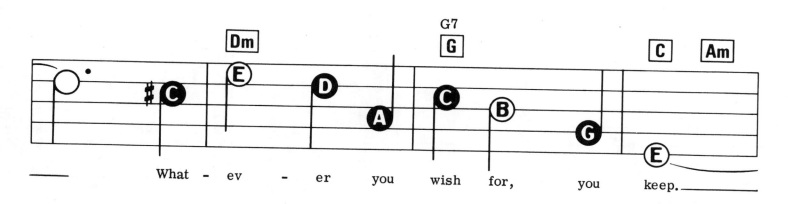

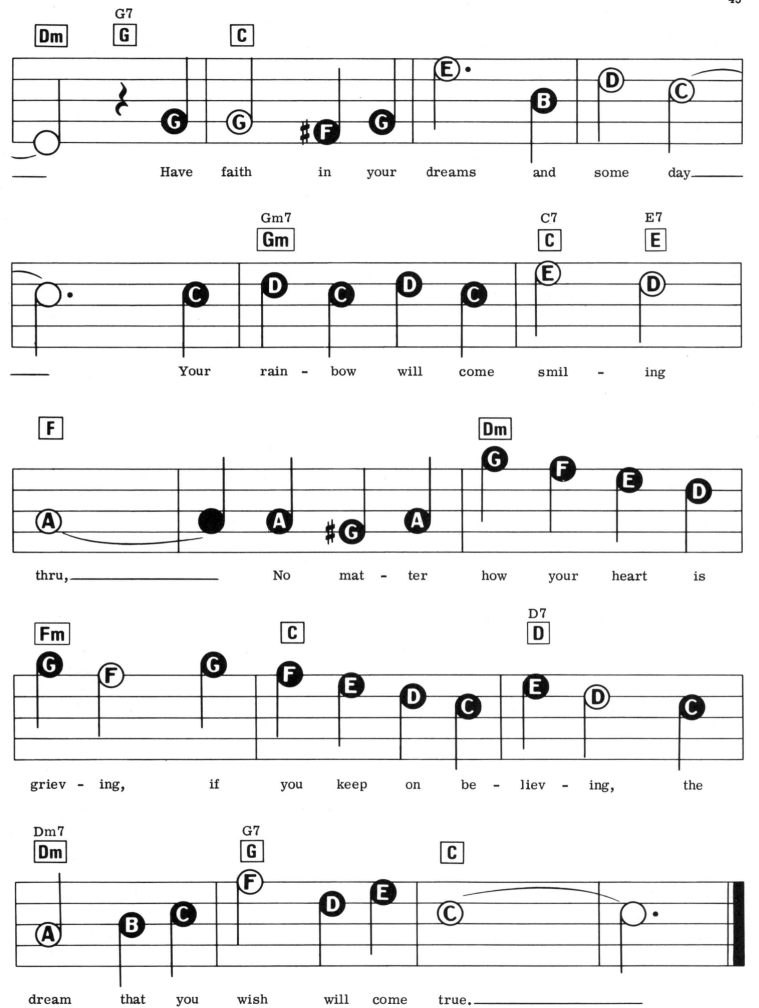

(I Love You)
For Sentimental Reasons

Registration 1
Rhythm: Fox Trot or Swing

Words by Deek Watson
Music by William Best

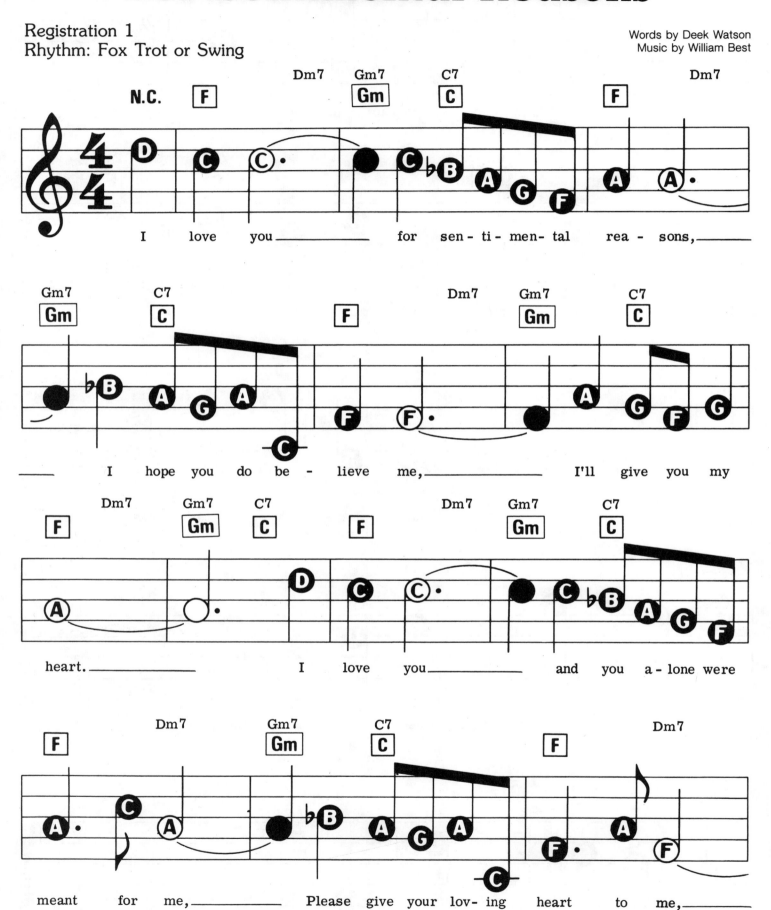

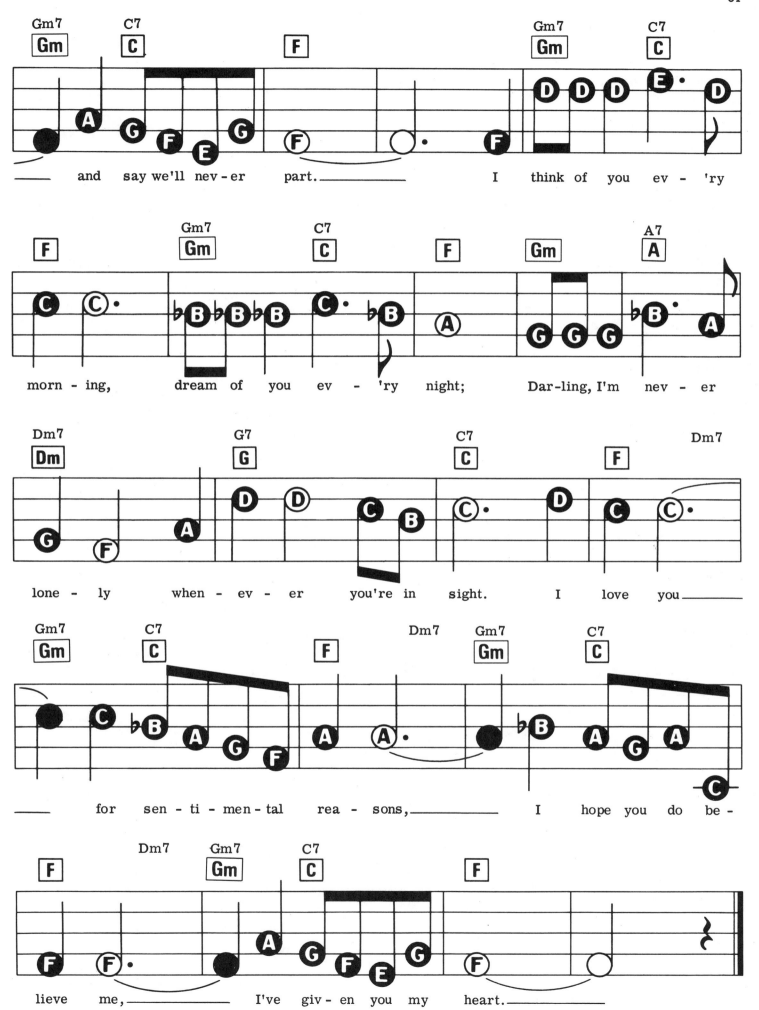

God Bless' the Child

Registration 4
Rhythm: Ballad or Fox Trot

Words and Music by
Arthur Herzog Jr. and Billie Holiday

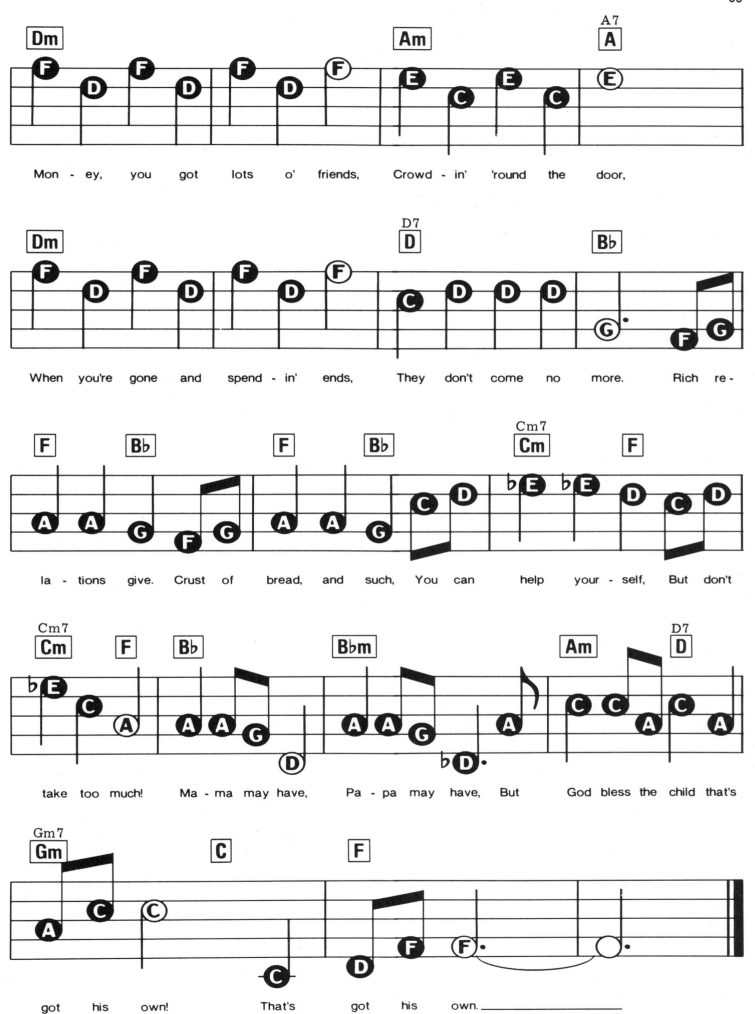

Have I Told You Lately That I Love You

Registration 10
Rhythm: Country Western or Ballad

Words and Music by
Scott Wiseman

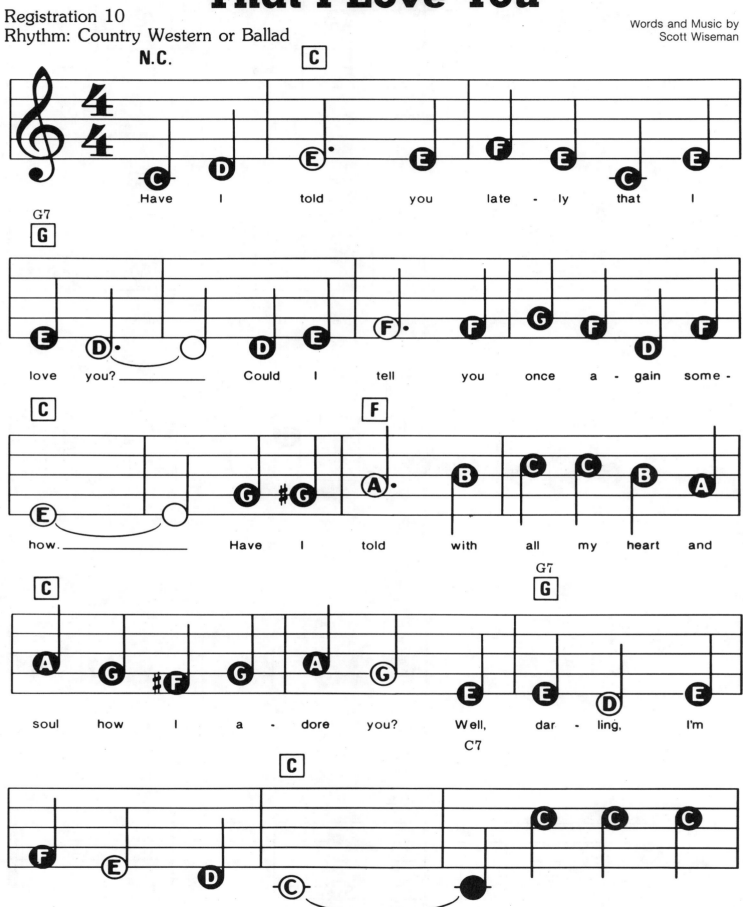

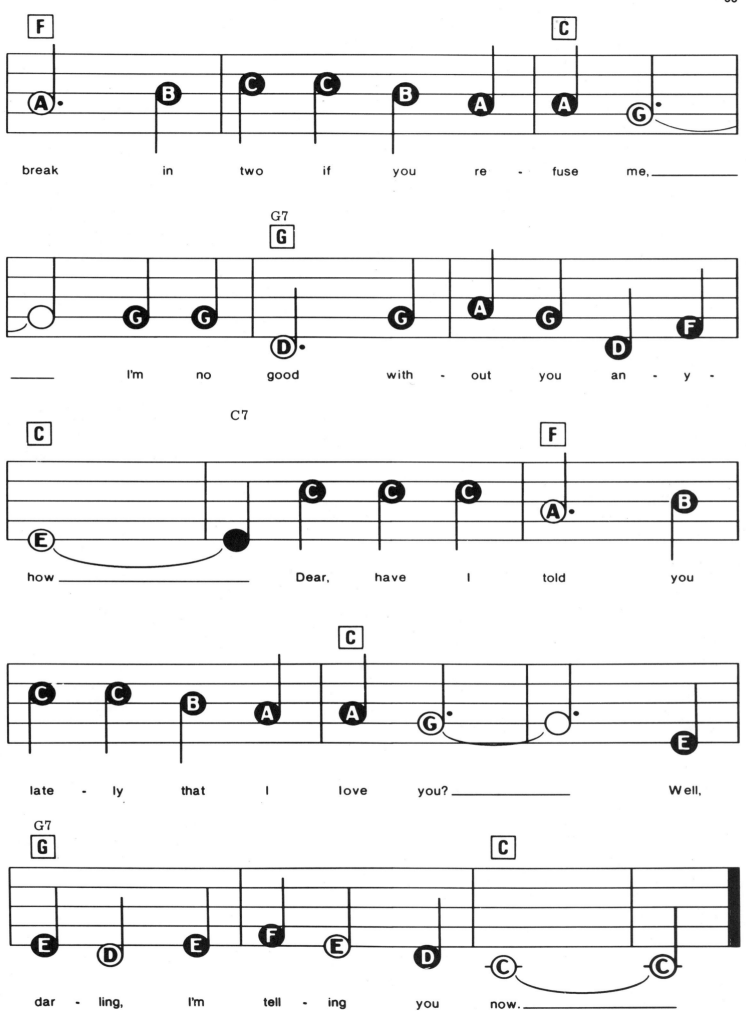

I'll Remember April

Registration 3
Rhythm: Swing

Words and Music by Don Raye,
Gene De Paul and Pat Johnson

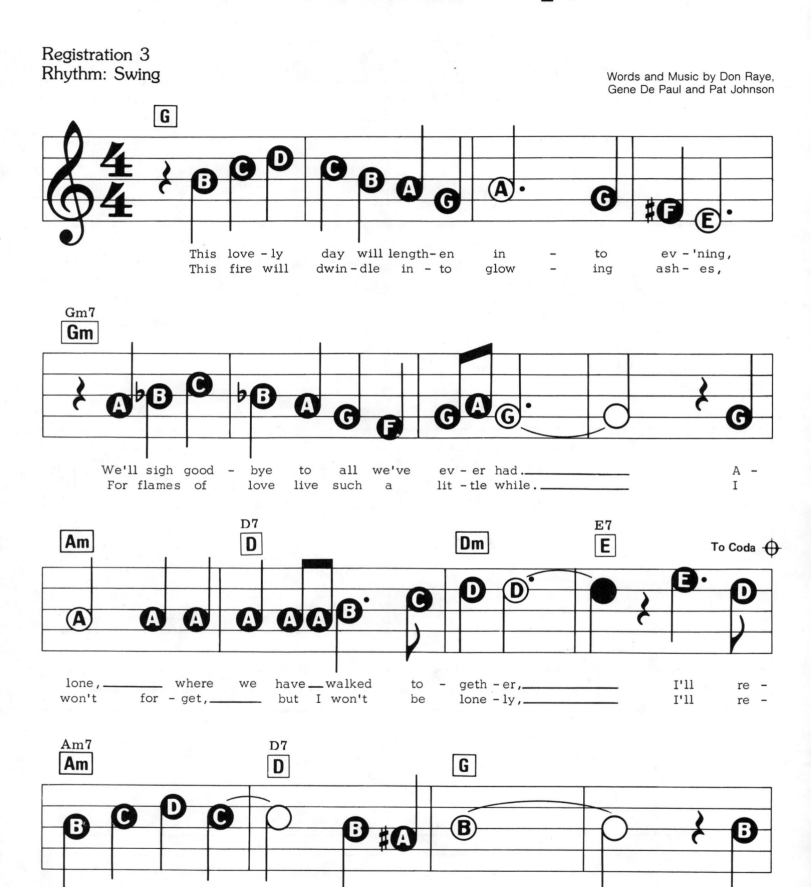

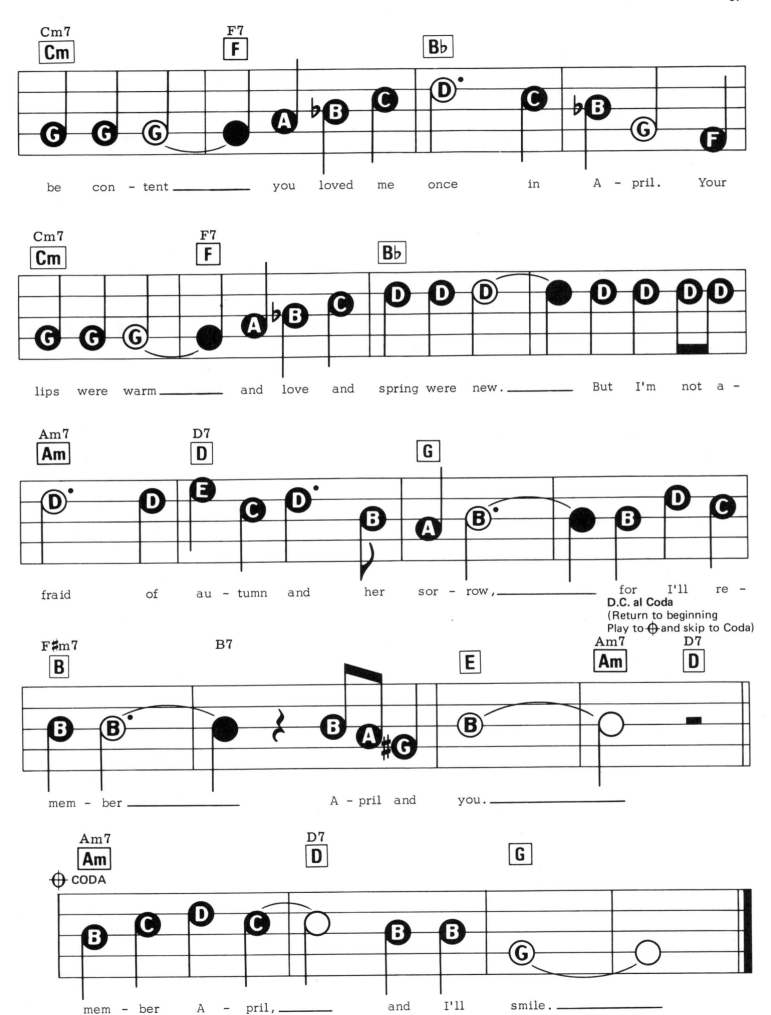

I'm Beginning to See the Light

Registration 4
Rhythm: Fox Trot or Swing

Words and Music by Harry James, Duke Ellington,
Johnny Hodges and Don George

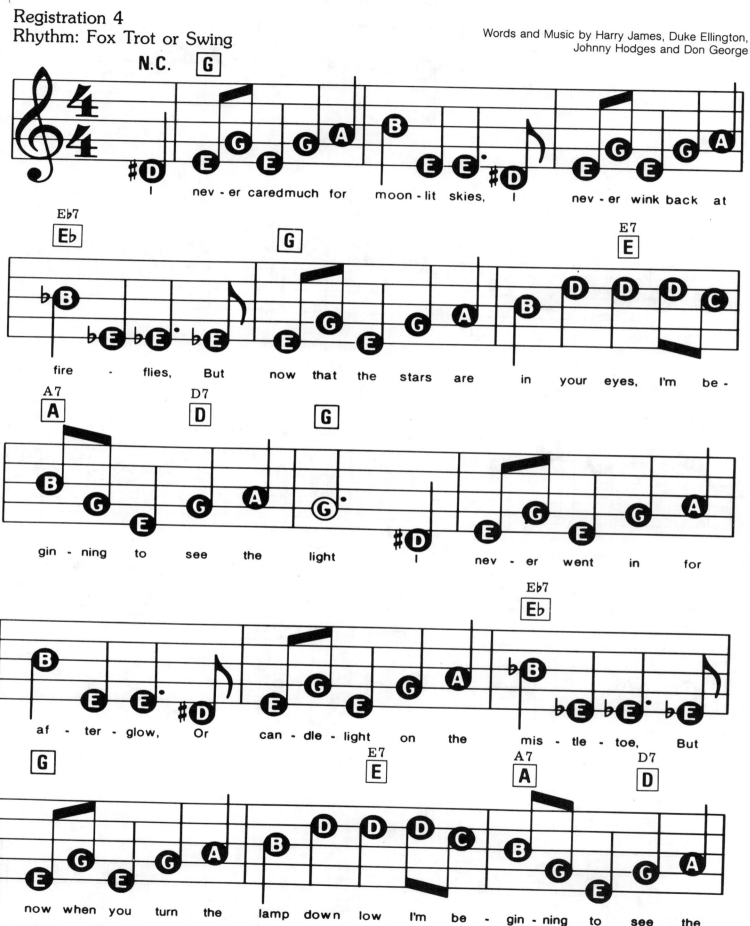

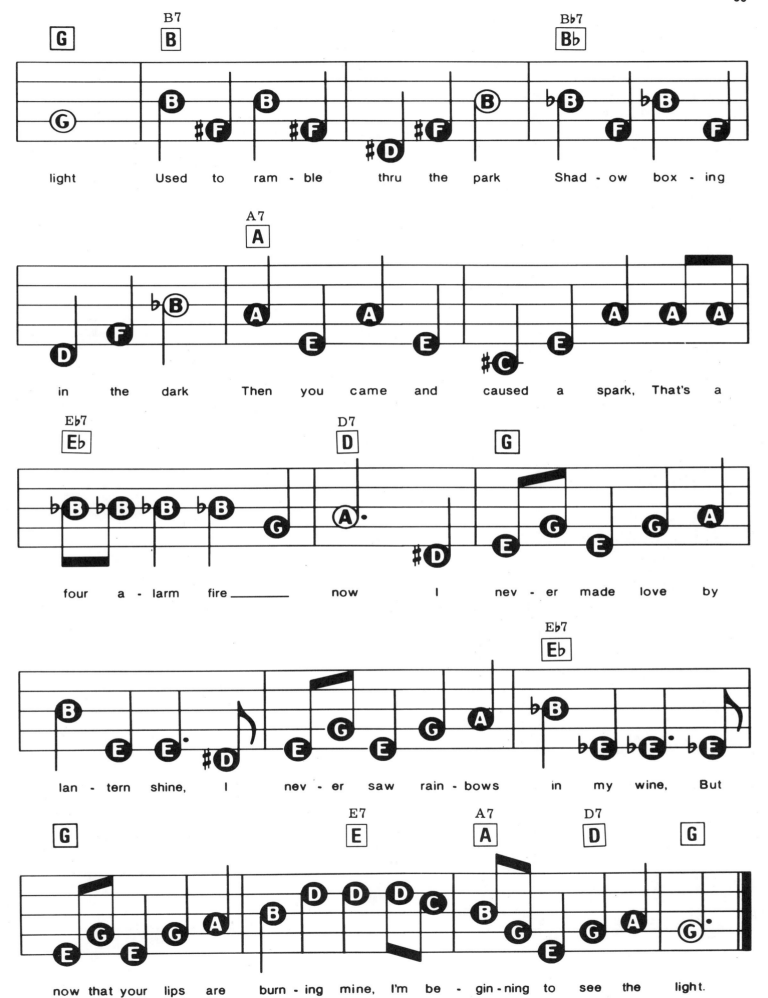

I've Got a Lovely Bunch
of Coconuts

Registration 4
Rhythm: 6/8 March

Words and Music by
Fred Heatherton

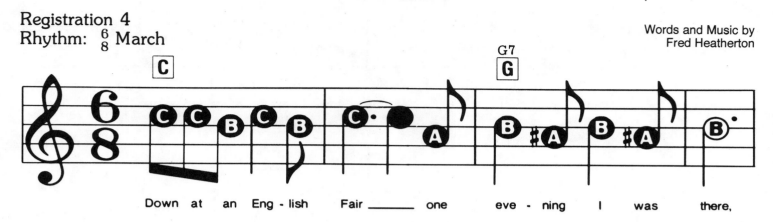

Down at an Eng-lish Fair _____ one eve-ning I was there,

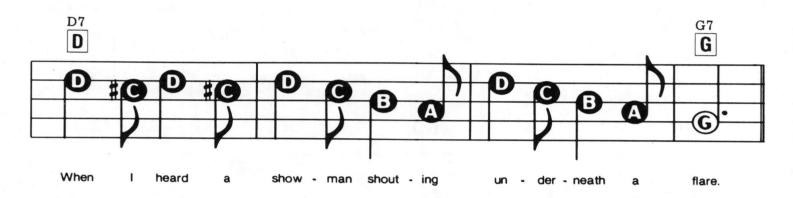

When I heard a show-man shout-ing un-der-neath a flare.

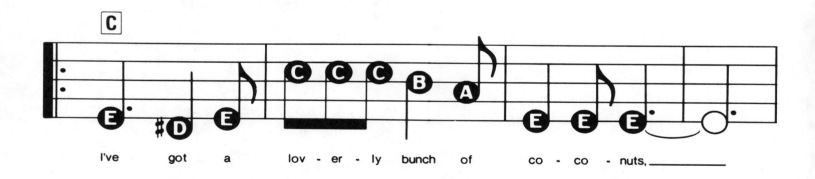

I've got a lov-er-ly bunch of co - co - nuts, _____

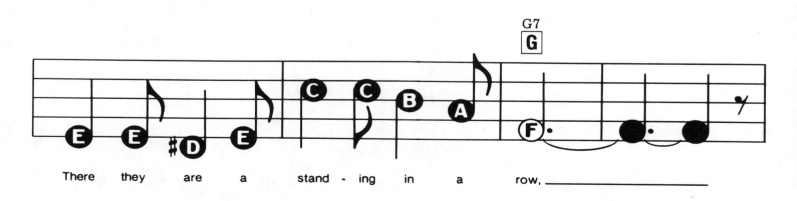

There they are a stand-ing in a row, _____

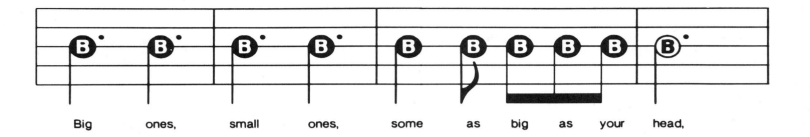

Big ones, small ones, some as big as your head,

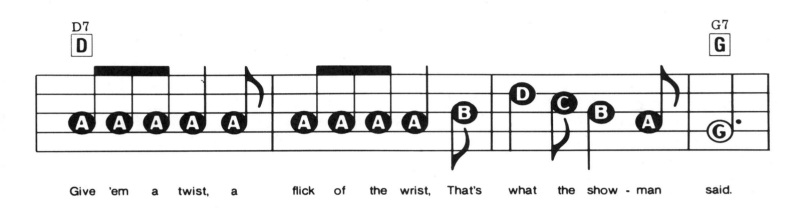

Give 'em a twist, a flick of the wrist, That's what the show - man said.

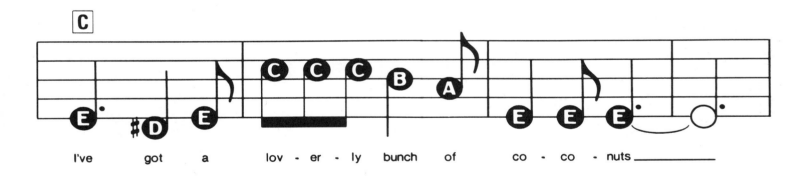

I've got a lov - er - ly bunch of co - co - nuts _____

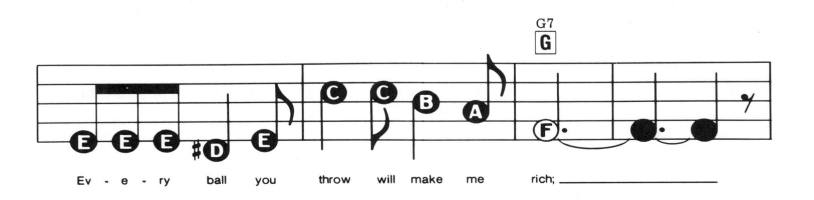

Ev - e - ry ball you throw will make me rich; _____

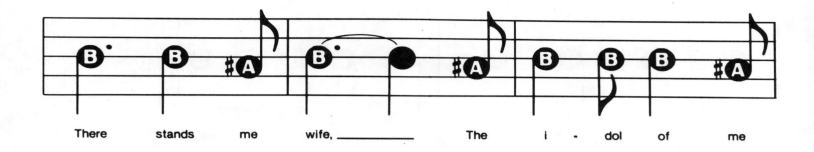

There stands me wife, _____ The i - dol of me

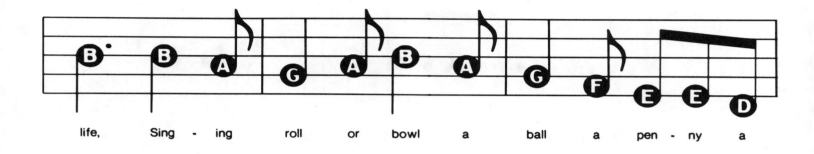

life, Sing - ing roll or bowl a ball a pen - ny a

C

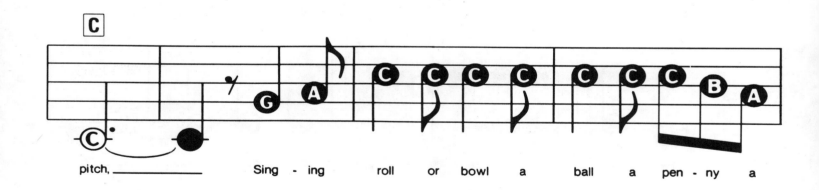

pitch, _____ Sing - ing roll or bowl a ball a pen - ny a

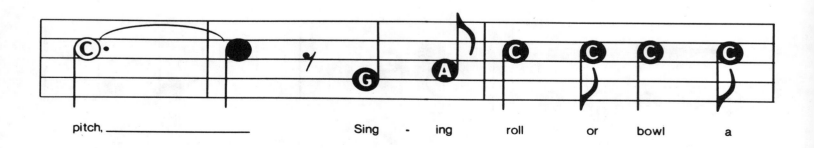

pitch, _____ Sing - ing roll or bowl a

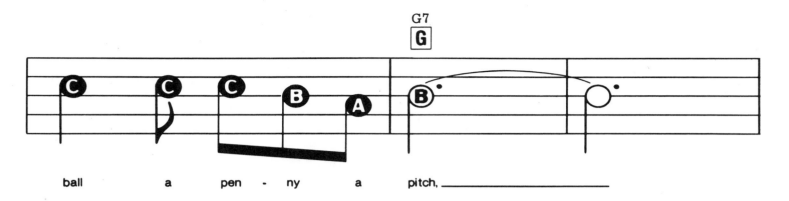

ball   a   pen - ny   a   pitch, _____

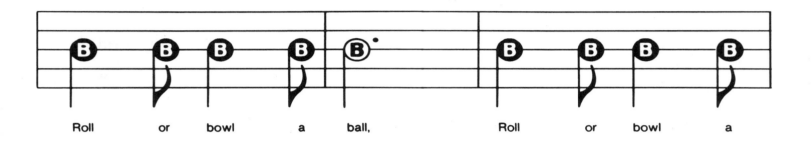

Roll   or   bowl   a   ball,   Roll   or   bowl   a

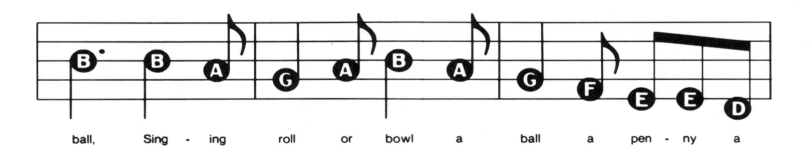

ball,   Sing - ing   roll   or   bowl   a   ball   a   pen - ny   a

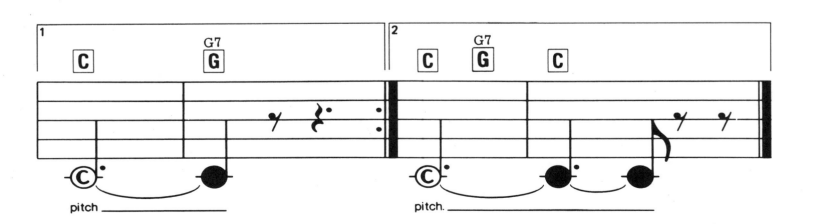

pitch _____   pitch. _____

If I Loved You
from CAROUSEL

Registration 2
Rhythm: Ballad

Lyrics by Oscar Hammerstein II
Music by Richard Rodgers

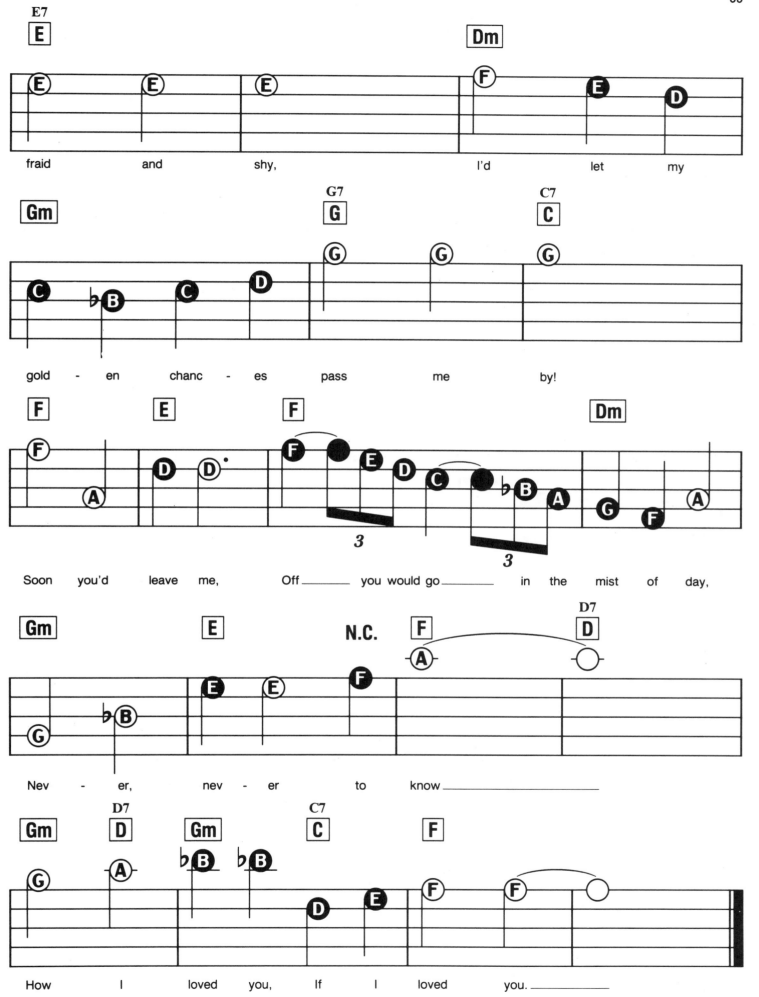

It Might as Well Be Spring
from STATE FAIR

Lyrics by Oscar Hammerstein II
Music by Richard Rodgers

Registration 3
Rhythm: Ballad

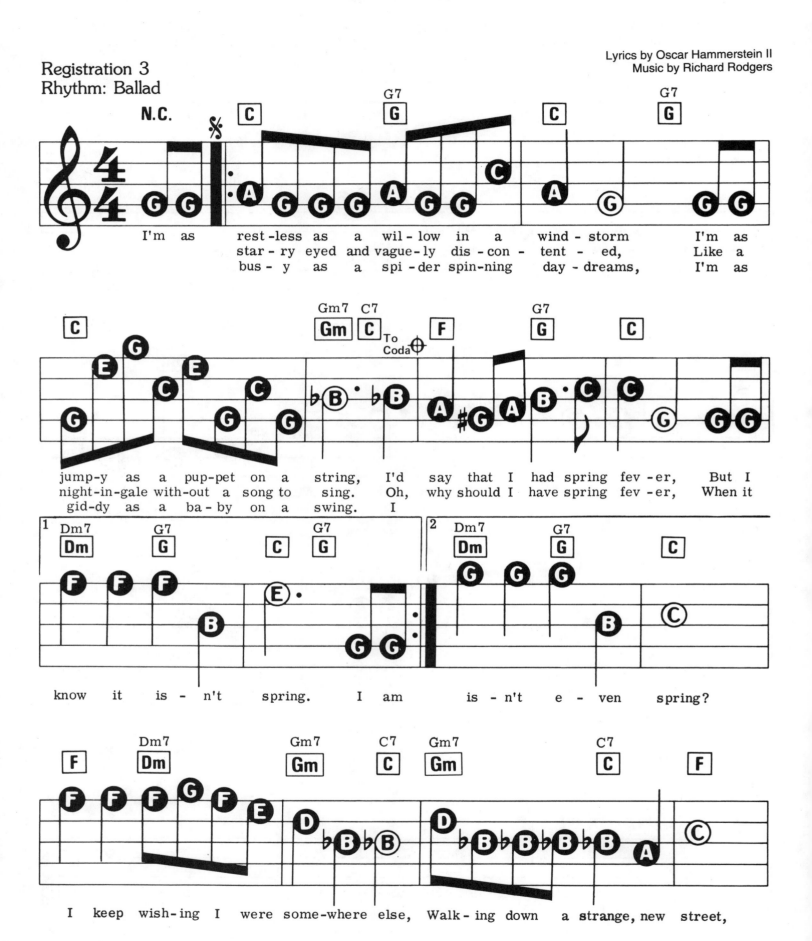

I'm as rest-less as a wil-low in a wind-storm I'm as
star-ry eyed and vague-ly dis-con-tent-ed, Like a
bus-y as a spi-der spin-ning day-dreams, I'm as

jump-y as a pup-pet on a string, I'd say that I had spring fev-er, But I
night-in-gale with-out a song to sing. Oh, why should I have spring fev-er, When it
gid-dy as a ba-by on a swing. I

know it is-n't spring. I am

is-n't e-ven spring?

I keep wish-ing I were some-where else, Walk-ing down a strange, new street,

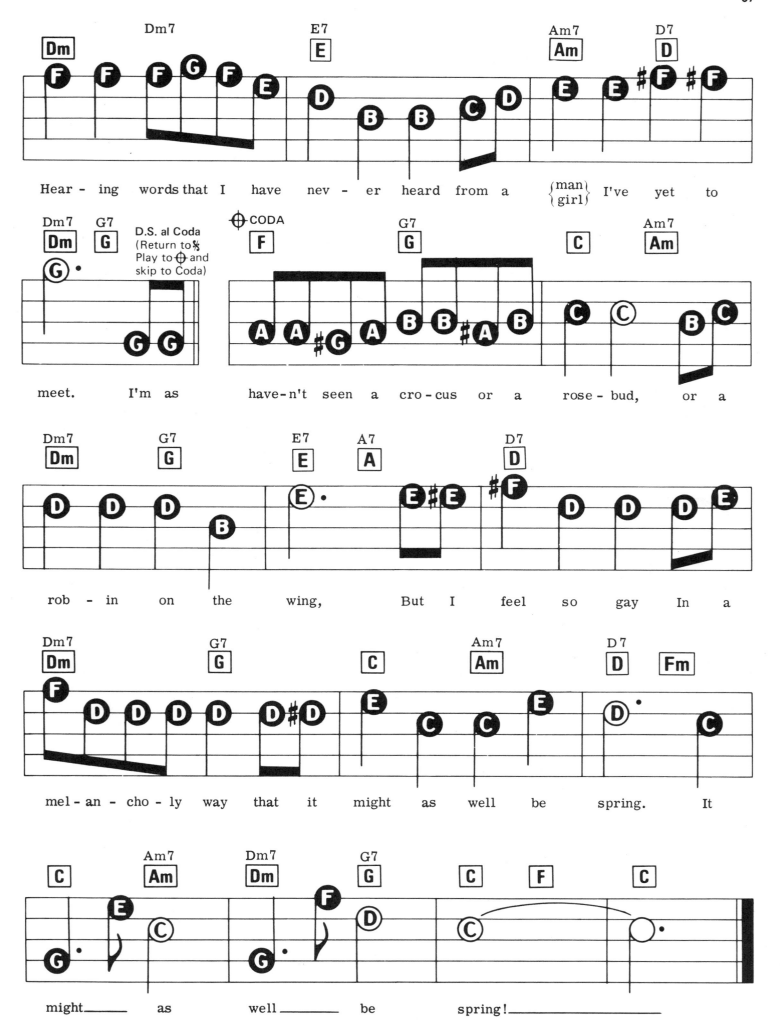

It's a Grand Night for Singing
from STATE FAIR

Registration 5
Rhythm: Waltz

Words by Oscar Hammerstein II
Music by Richard Rodgers

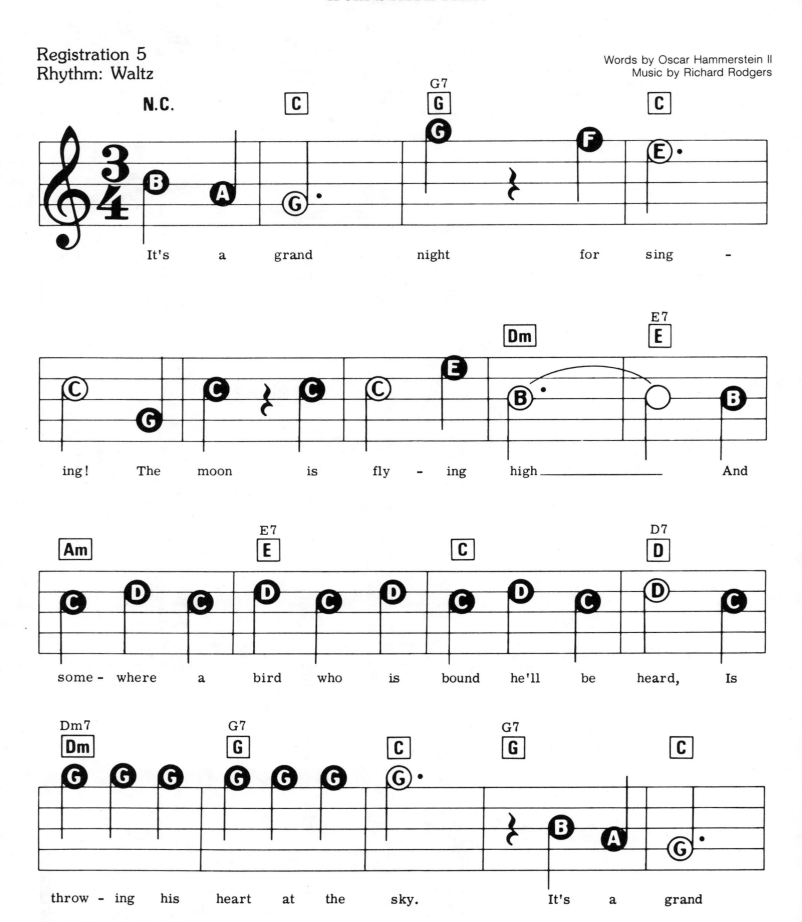

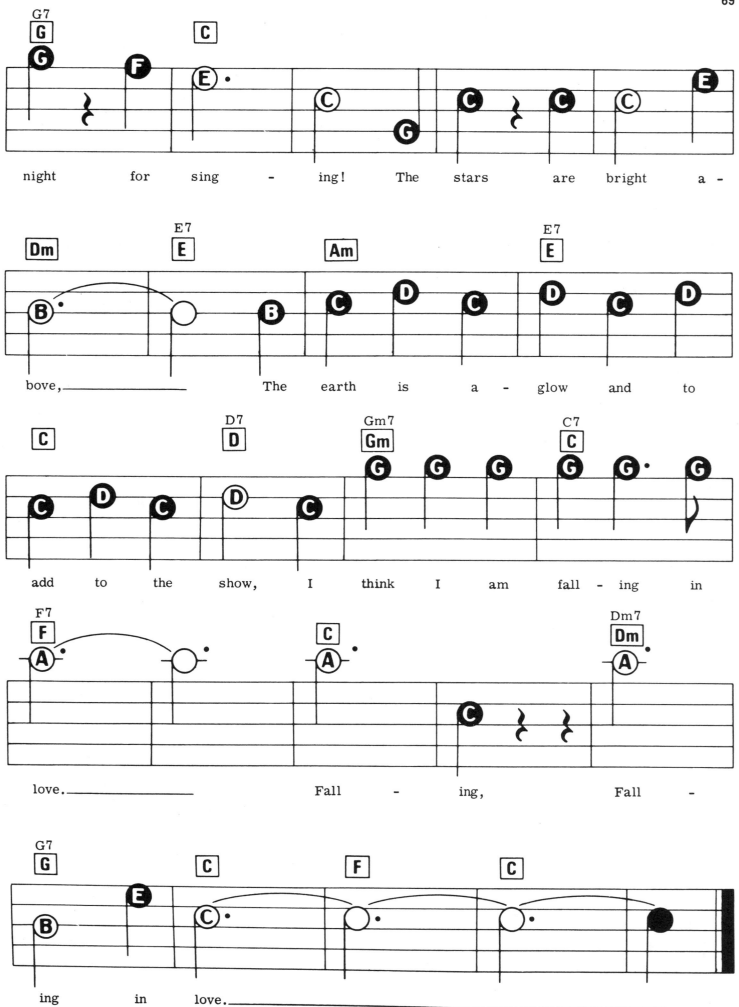

It's a Most Unusual Day
from A DATE WITH JUDY

Registration 5
Rhythm: Waltz

Words by Harold Adamson
Music by Jimmy McHugh

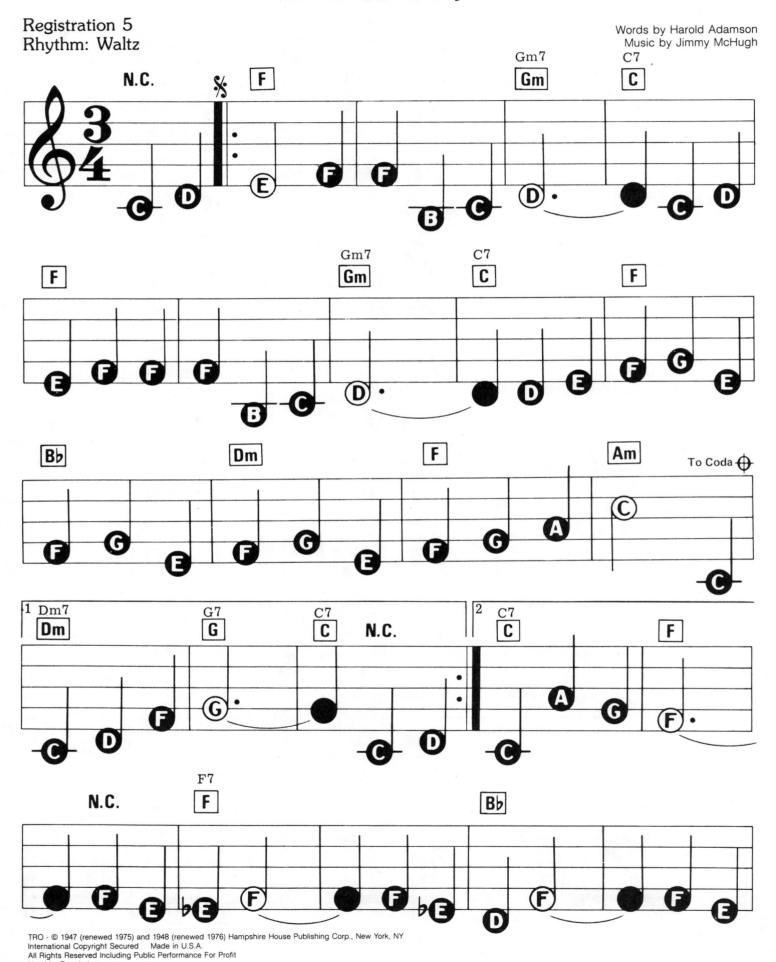

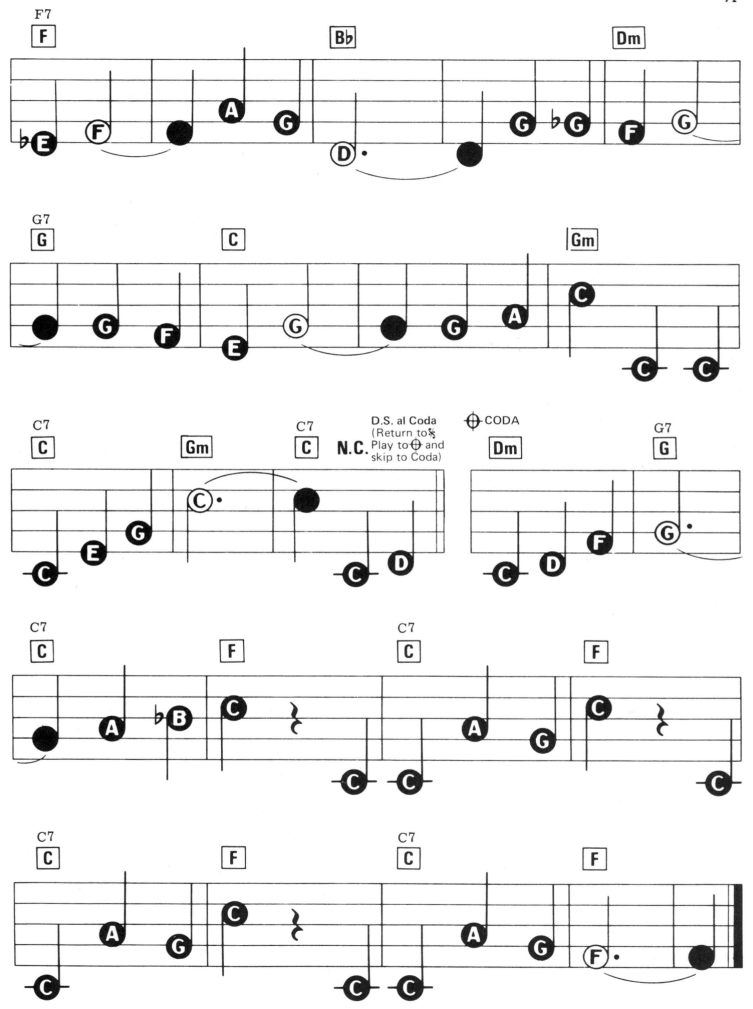

The Last Time I Saw Paris
from LADY, BE GOOD

Registration 10
Rhythm: Ballad or Swing

Words by Oscar Hammerstein II
Music by Jerome Kern

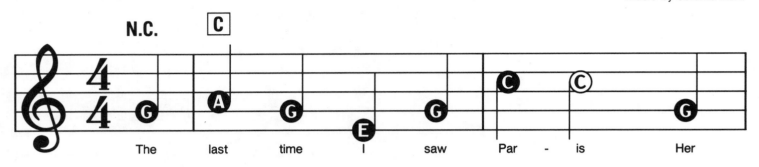

The last time I saw Par - is Her

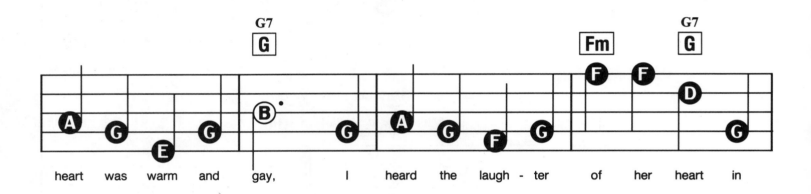

heart was warm and gay, I heard the laugh - ter of her heart in

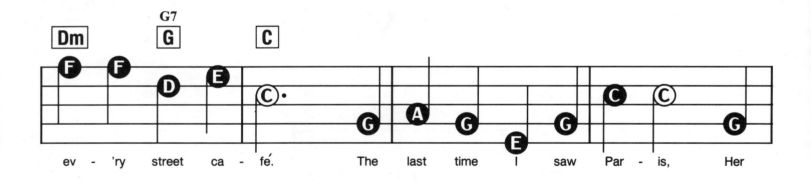

ev - 'ry street ca - fé. The last time I saw Par - is, Her

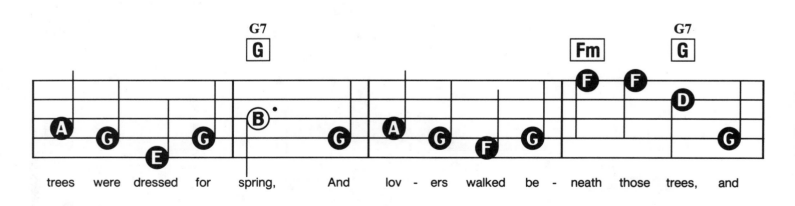

trees were dressed for spring, And lov - ers walked be - neath those trees, and

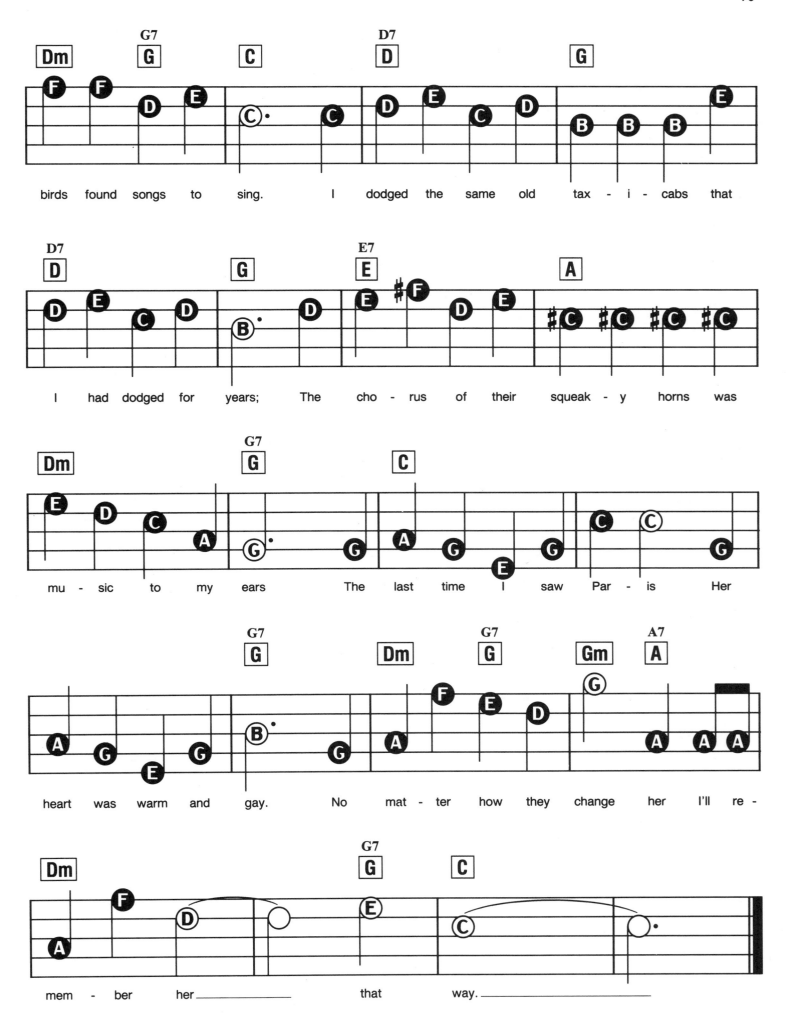

Long Ago
(And Far Away)
from COVER GIRL

Registration 3
Rhythm: Ballad or Swing

Words by Ira Gershwin
Music by Jerome Kern

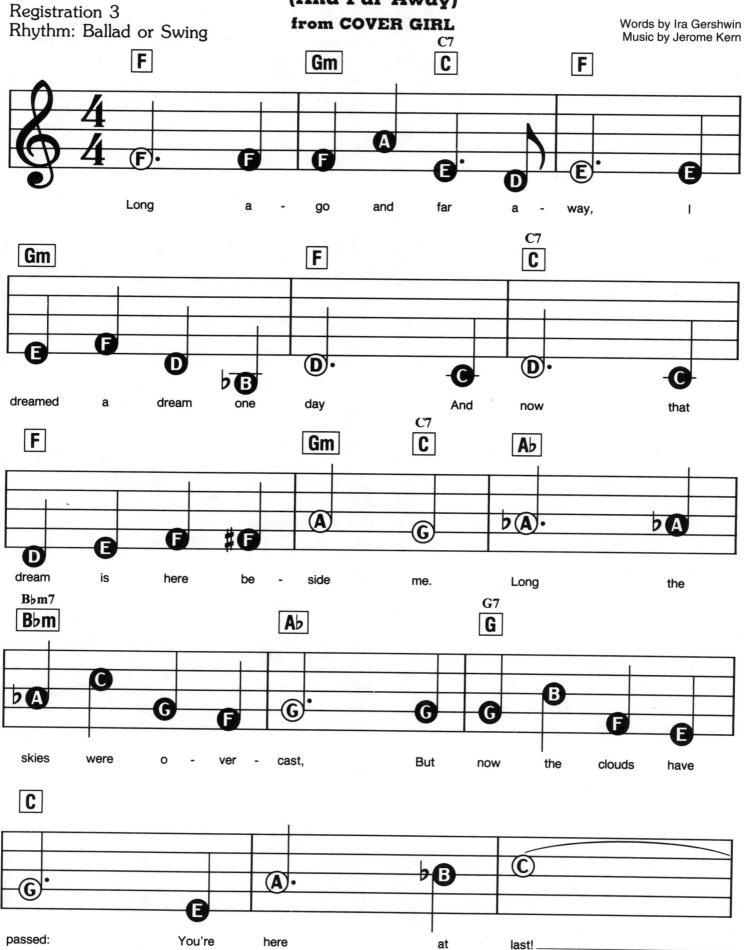

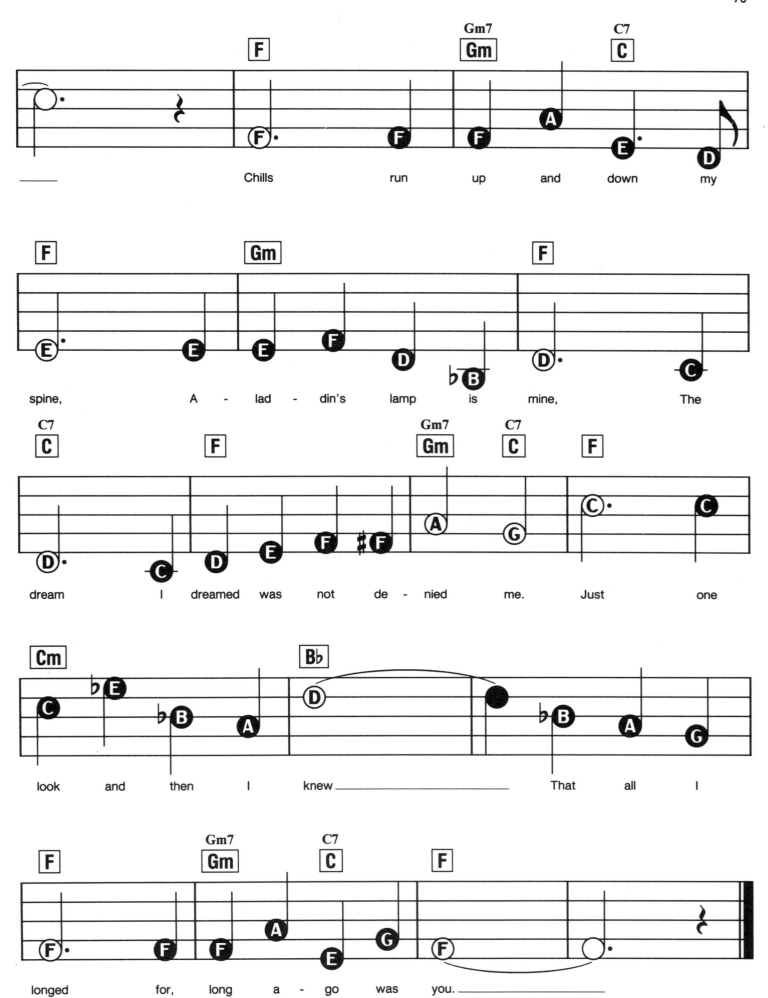

Mairzy Doats

Registration 5
Rhythm: Fox Trot or Swing

Words and Music by Milton Drake,
Al Hoffman and Jerry Livingston

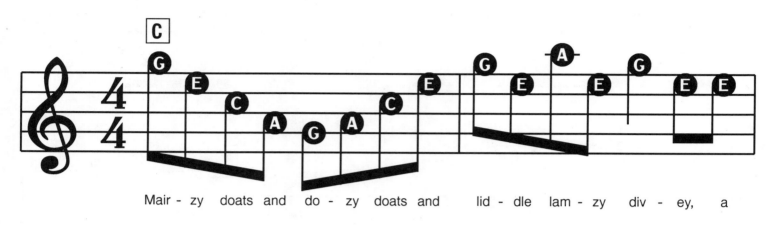

Mair - zy doats and do - zy doats and lid - dle lam - zy div - ey, a

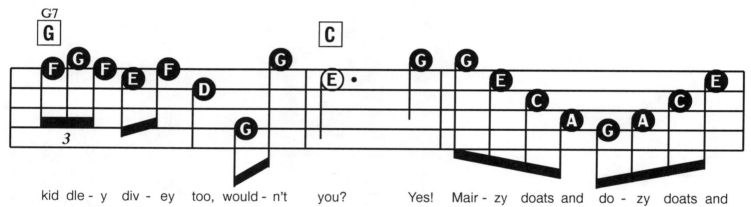

kid dle - y div - ey too, would - n't you? Yes! Mair - zy doats and do - zy doats and

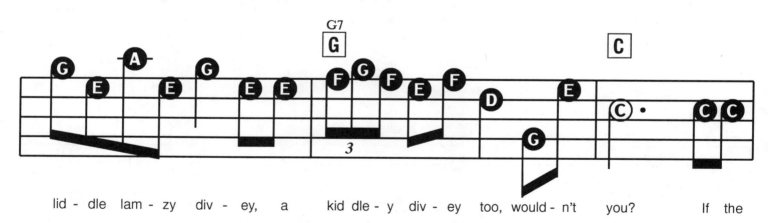

lid - dle lam - zy div - ey, a kid dle - y div - ey too, would - n't you? If the

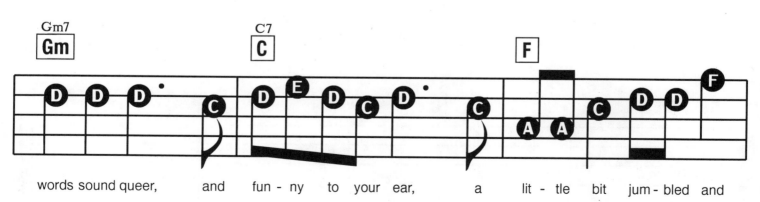

words sound queer, and fun - ny to your ear, a lit - tle bit jum - bled and

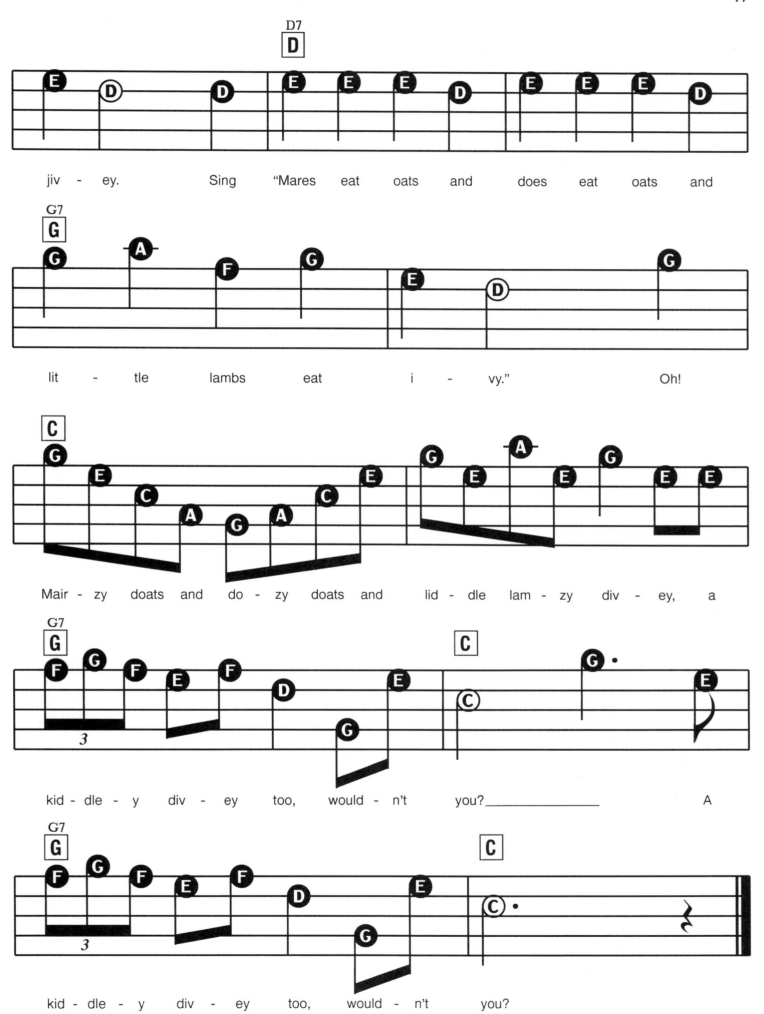

Moonlight Becomes You
from the Paramount Picture ROAD TO MOROCCO

Registration 1
Rhythm: Swing

Words by Johnny Burke
Music by James Van Heusen

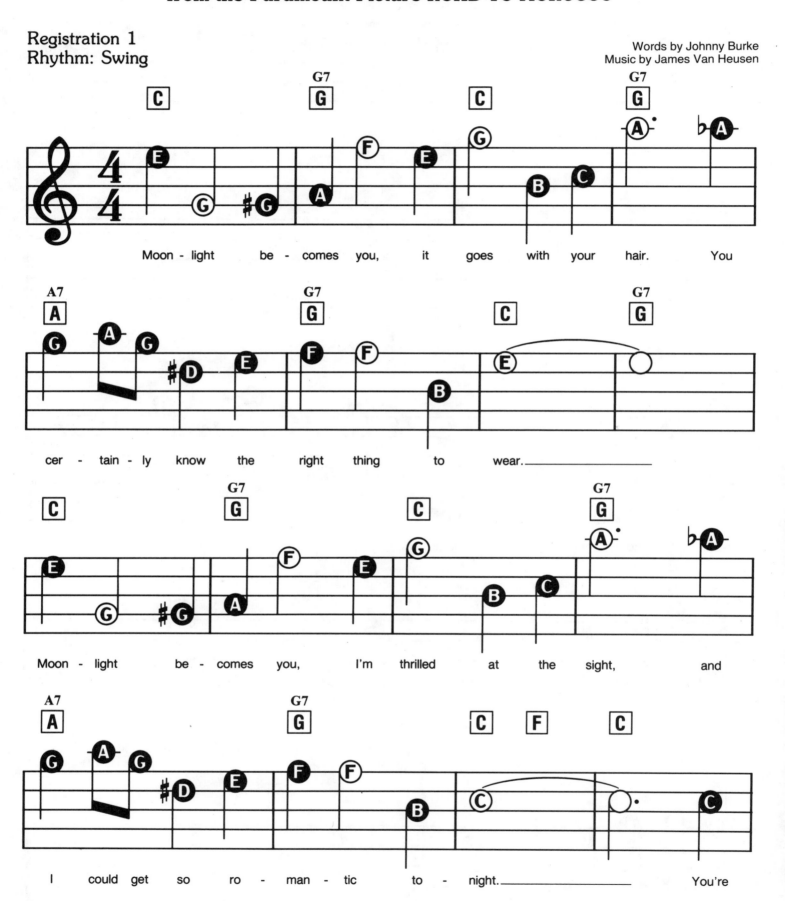

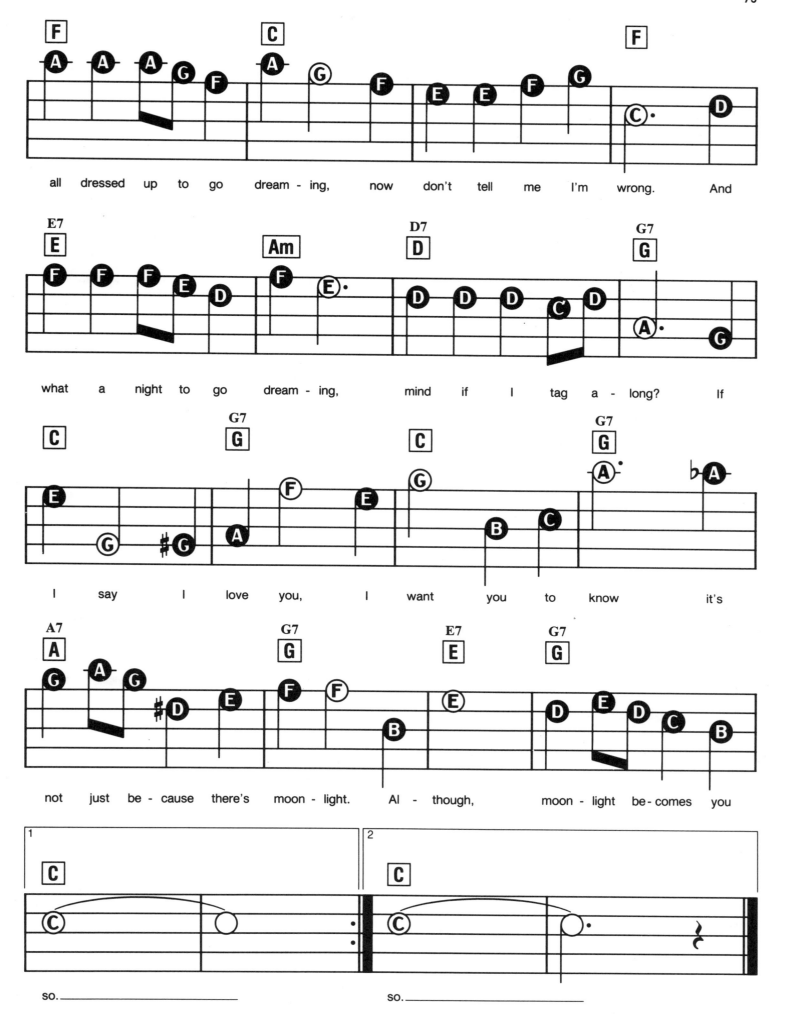

The Nearness of You
from the Paramount Picture ROMANCE IN THE DARK

Registration 9
Rhythm: Fox Trot or Swing

Words by Ned Washington
Music by Hoagy Carmichael

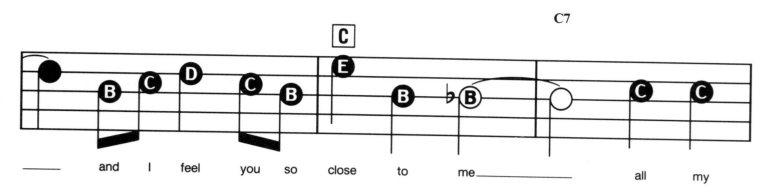

and I feel you so close to me———— all my

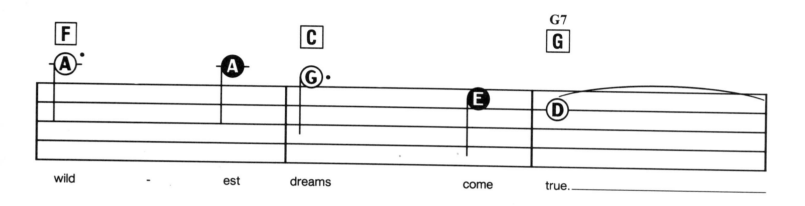

wild - est dreams come true.————

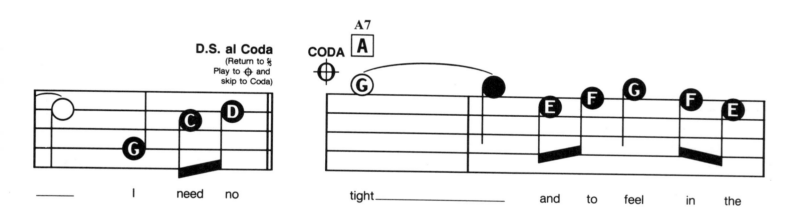

———— I need no   tight———————— and to feel in the

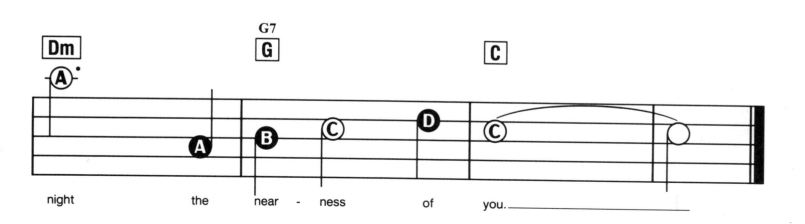

night   the near - ness of you.————

Oh, What a Beautiful Mornin'

from OKLAHOMA!

Registration 5
Rhythm: Waltz

Words by Oscar Hammerstein II
Music by Richard Rodgers

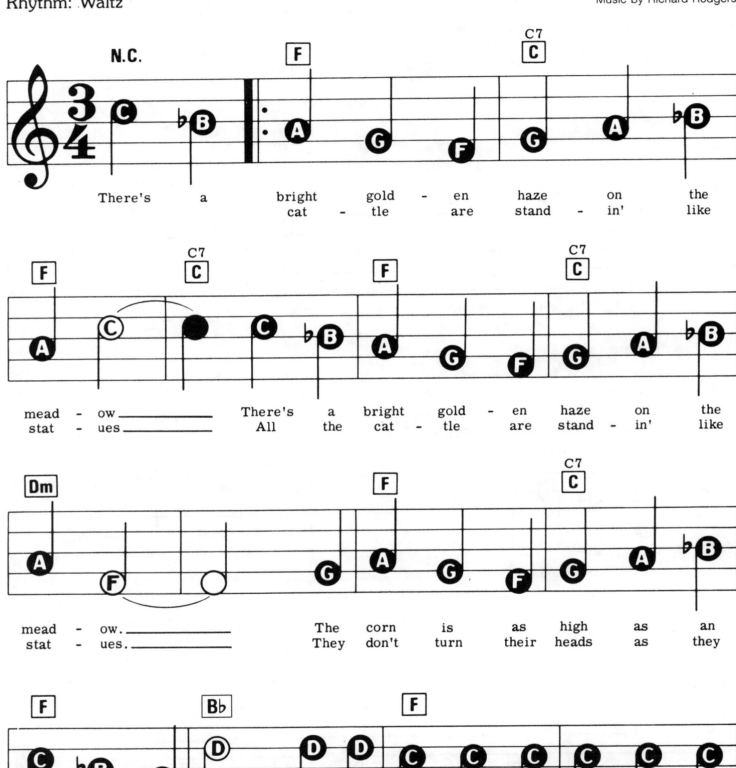

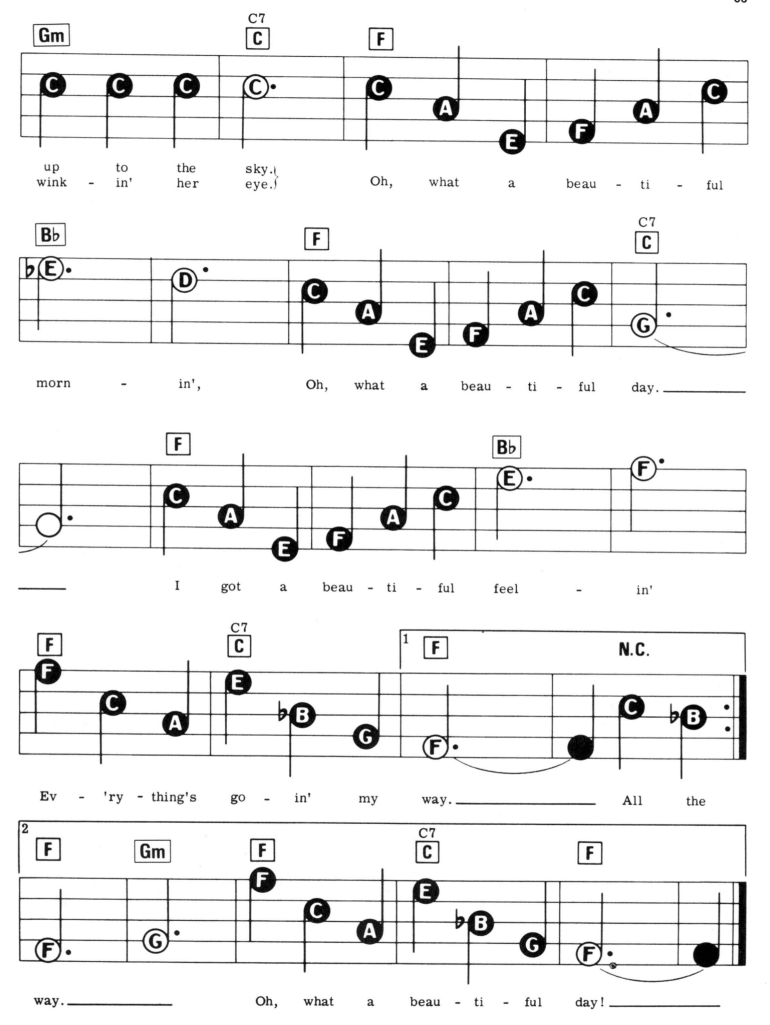

Oklahoma
from OKLAHOMA!

Registration 5
Rhythm: Fox Trot or Swing

Words by Oscar Hammerstein II
Music by Richard Rodgers

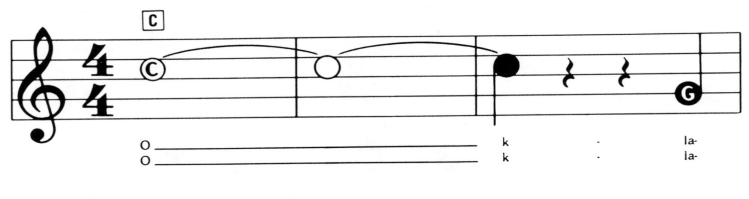

O _____ k - la-
O _____ k - la-

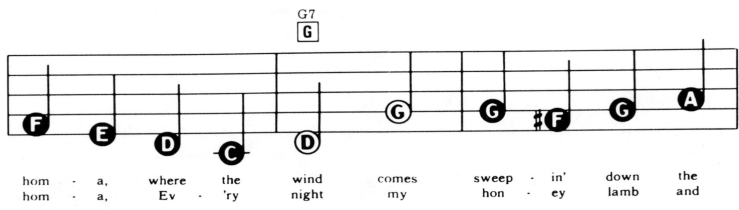

hom - a, where the wind comes sweep - in' down the
hom - a, Ev - 'ry night my hon - ey lamb and

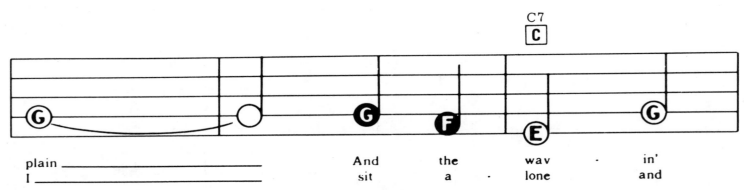

plain _____ And the wav - in'
I _____ sit a - lone and

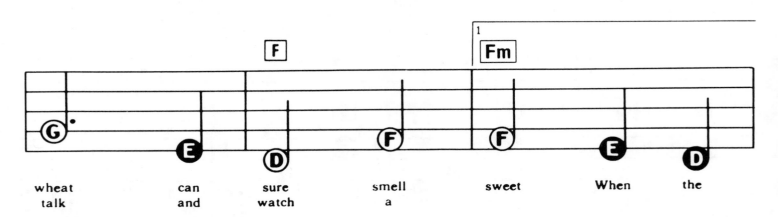

wheat can sure smell sweet When the
talk and watch a

85

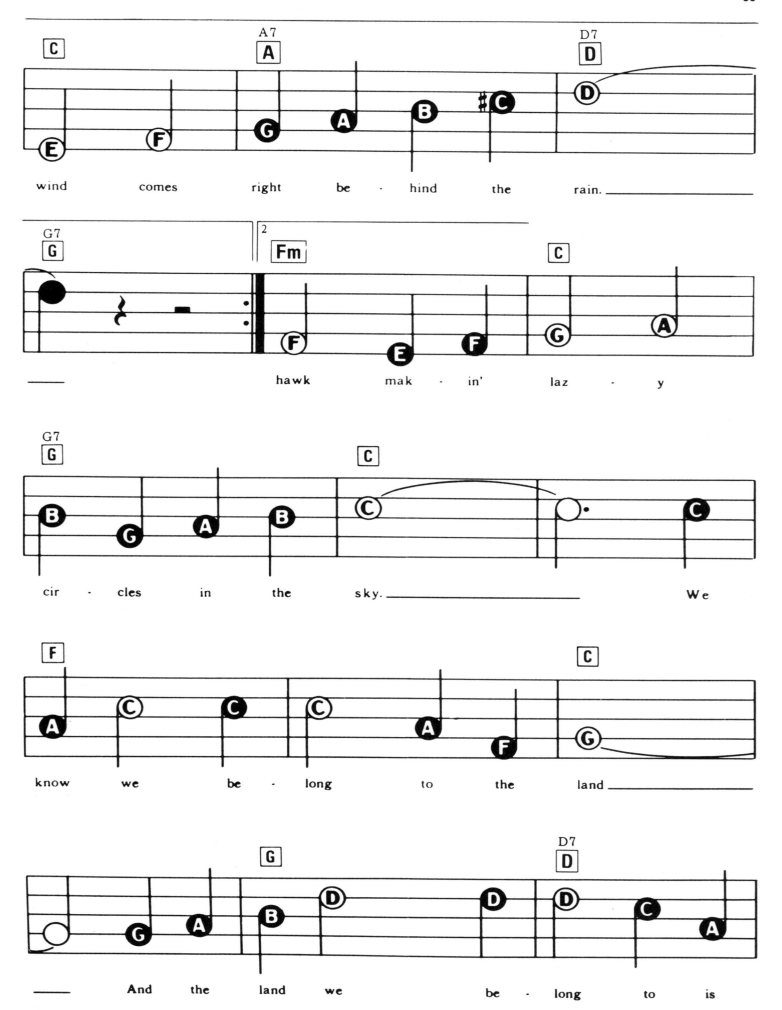

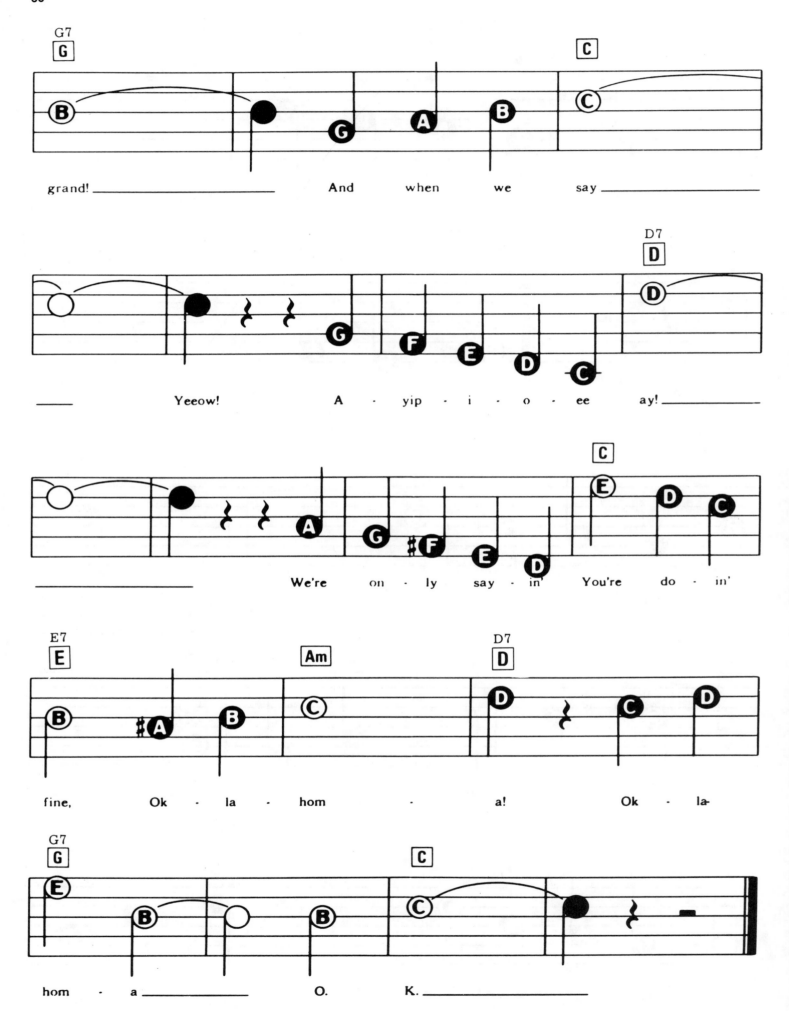

Opus One

Registration 7
Rhythm: Swing or Jazz

Words and Music by
Sy Oliver

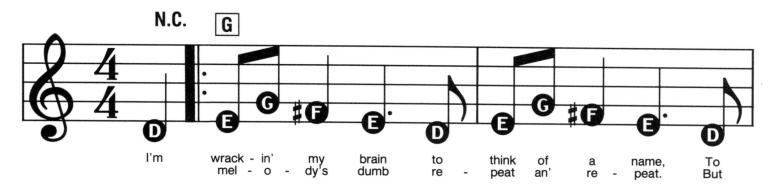

I'm wrack - in' my brain to think of a name, To
mel - o - dy's dumb re - peat an' re - peat. But

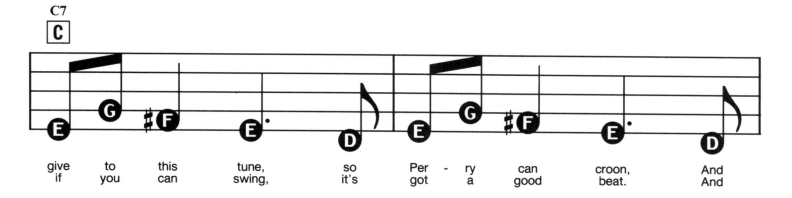

give to this tune, so Per - ry can croon, And
if you can swing, it's got a good beat. And

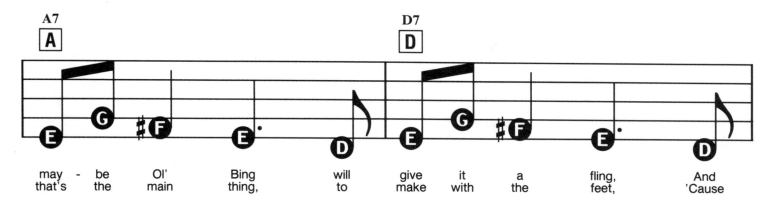

may - be Ol' Bing will give it a fling, And
that's the main thing, to make with the feet, 'Cause

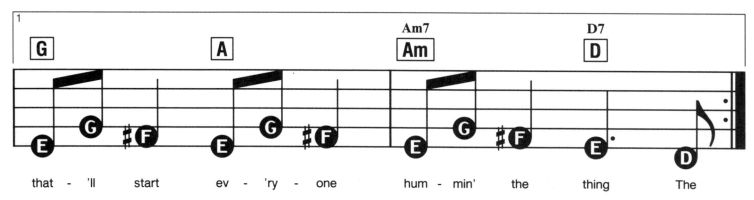

that - 'll start ev - 'ry - one hum - min' the thing The

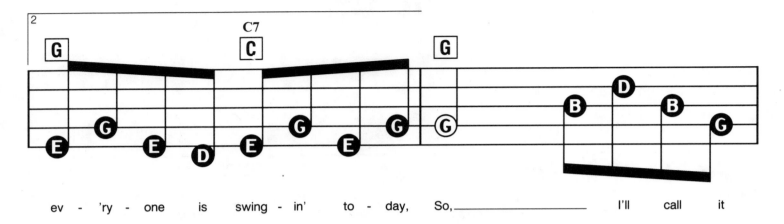

ev - 'ry - one is swing-in' to - day, So,＿＿＿＿＿＿ I'll call it

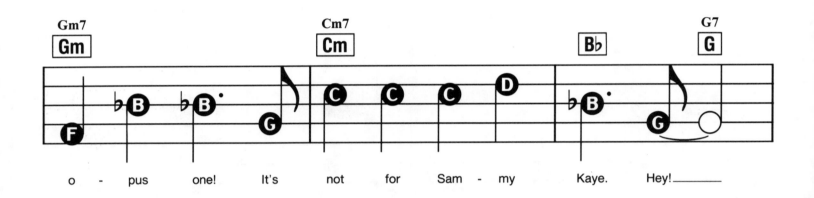

o - pus one! It's not for Sam - my Kaye. Hey!＿＿＿＿

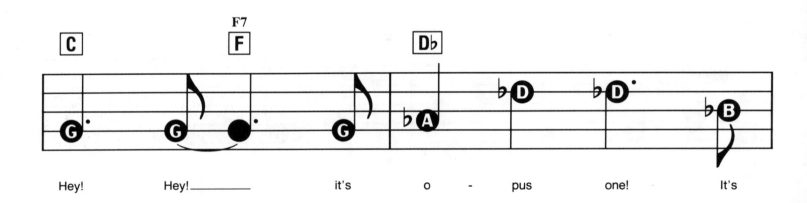

Hey! Hey!＿＿＿＿ it's o - pus one! It's

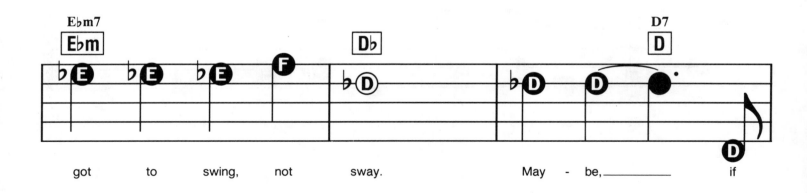

got to swing, not sway. May - be,＿＿＿＿ if

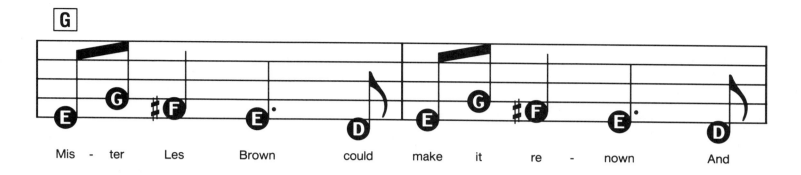

Mis - ter Les Brown could make it re - nown And

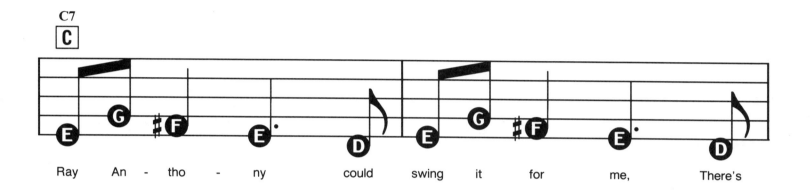

Ray An - tho - ny could swing it for me, There's

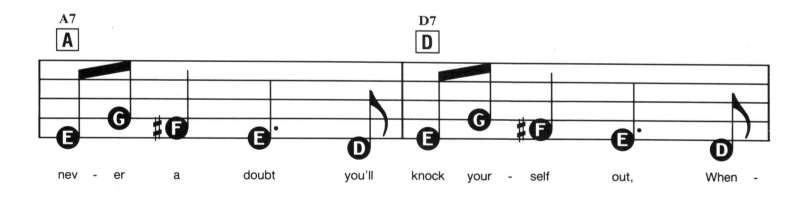

nev - er a doubt you'll knock your - self out, When -

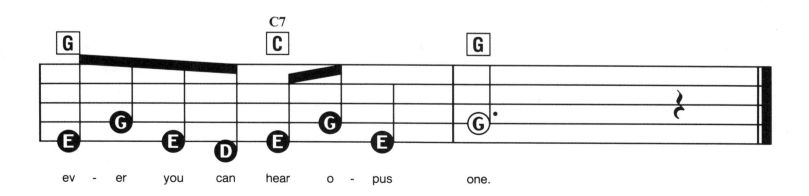

ev - er you can hear o - pus one.

On a Slow Boat to China

Registration 2
Rhythm: Swing

By Frank Loesser

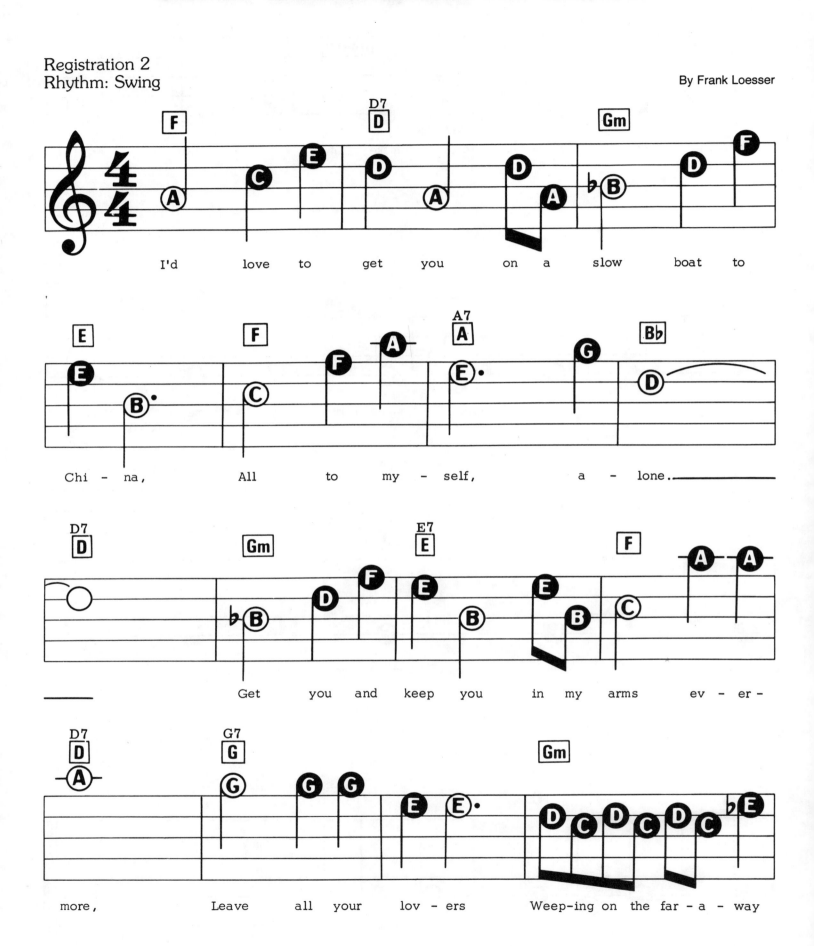

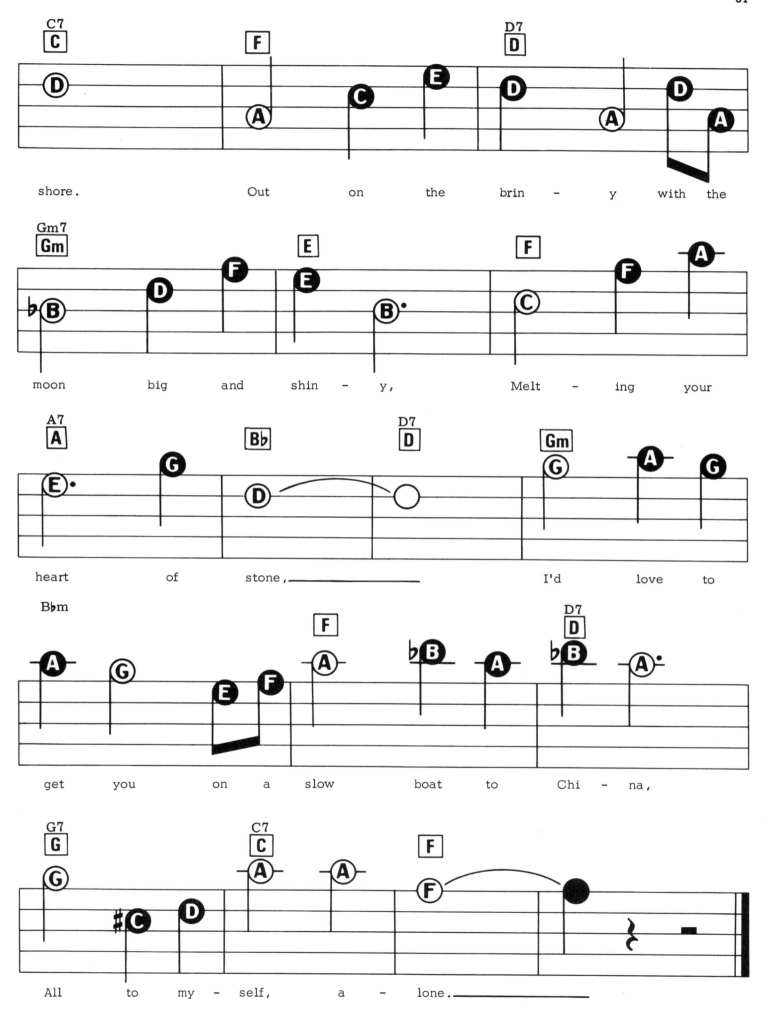

People Will Say We're in Love

from OKLAHOMA!

Registration 5
Rhythm: Fox Trot or Swing

Words by Oscar Hammerstein II
Music by Richard Rodgers

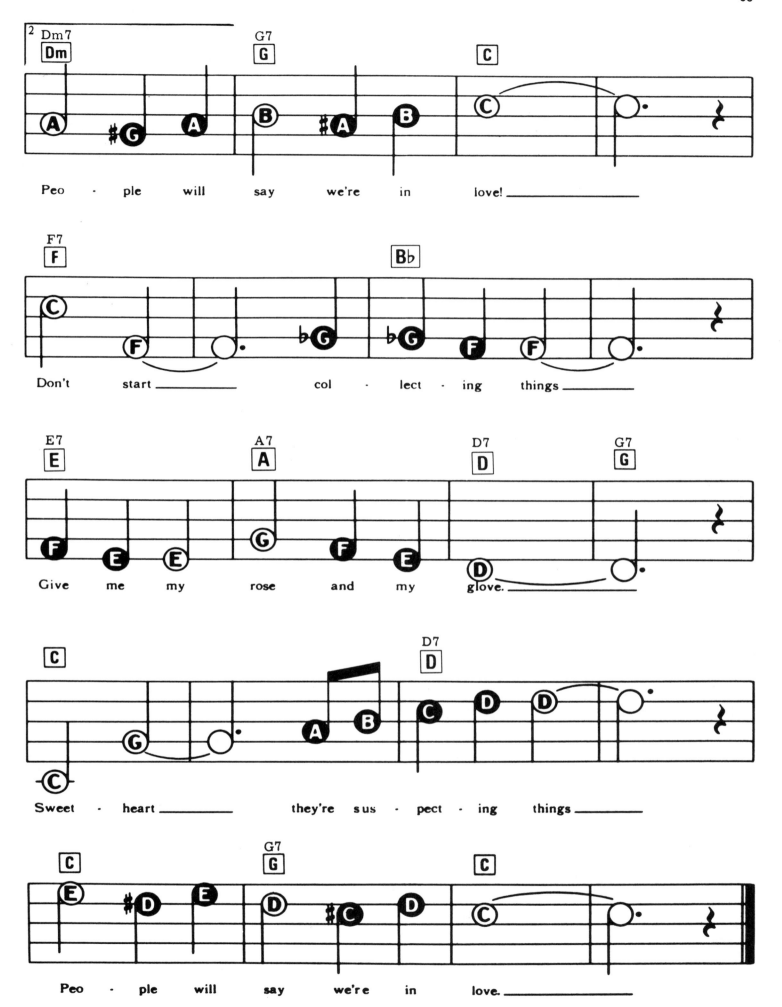

Some Enchanted Evening
from SOUTH PACIFIC

Registration 1
Rhythm: Fox Trot

Lyrics by Oscar Hammerstein II
Music by Richard Rodgers

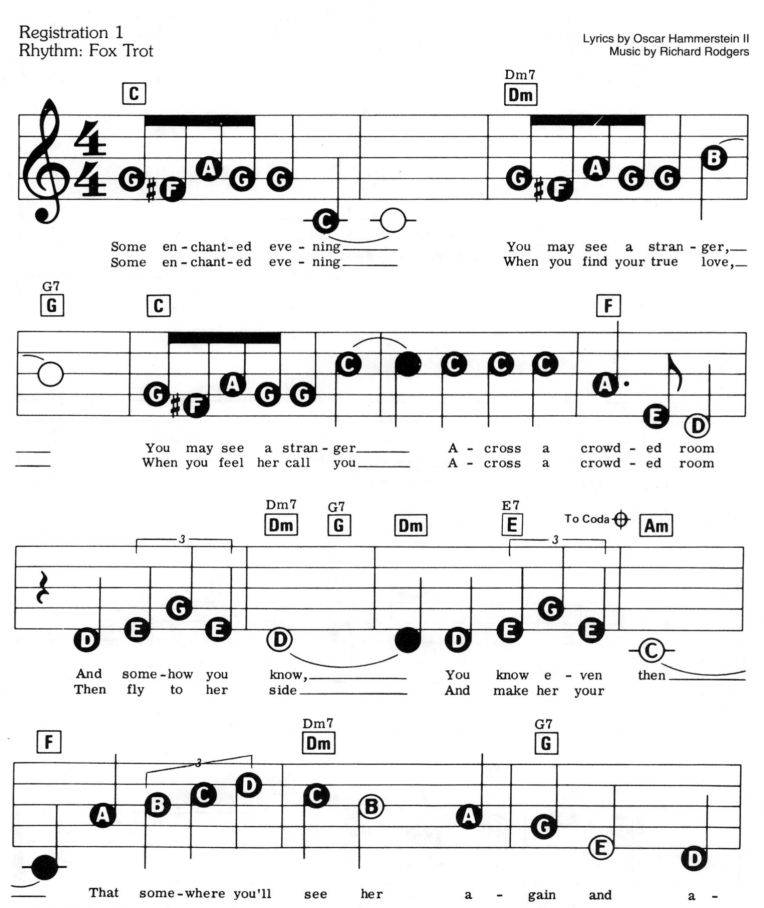

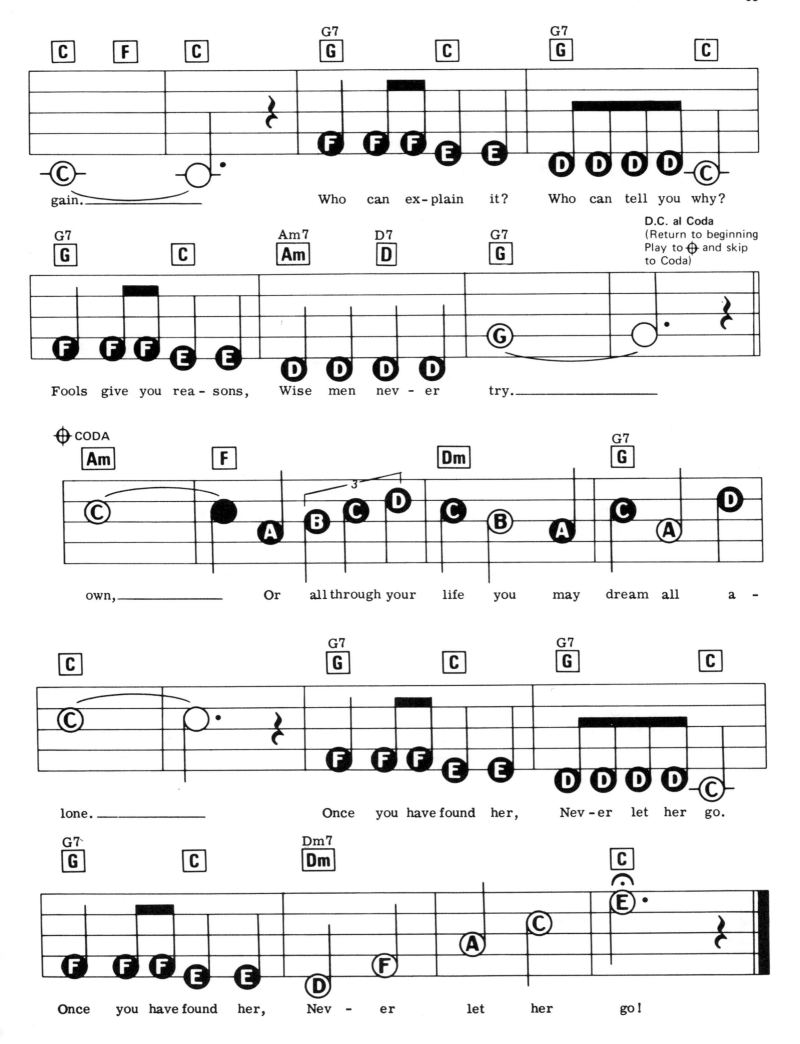

A Sunday Kind of Love

Registration 2
Rhythm: Swing or Jazz

Words and Music by Barbara Belle,
Louis Prima, Anita Leonard and Stan Rhodes

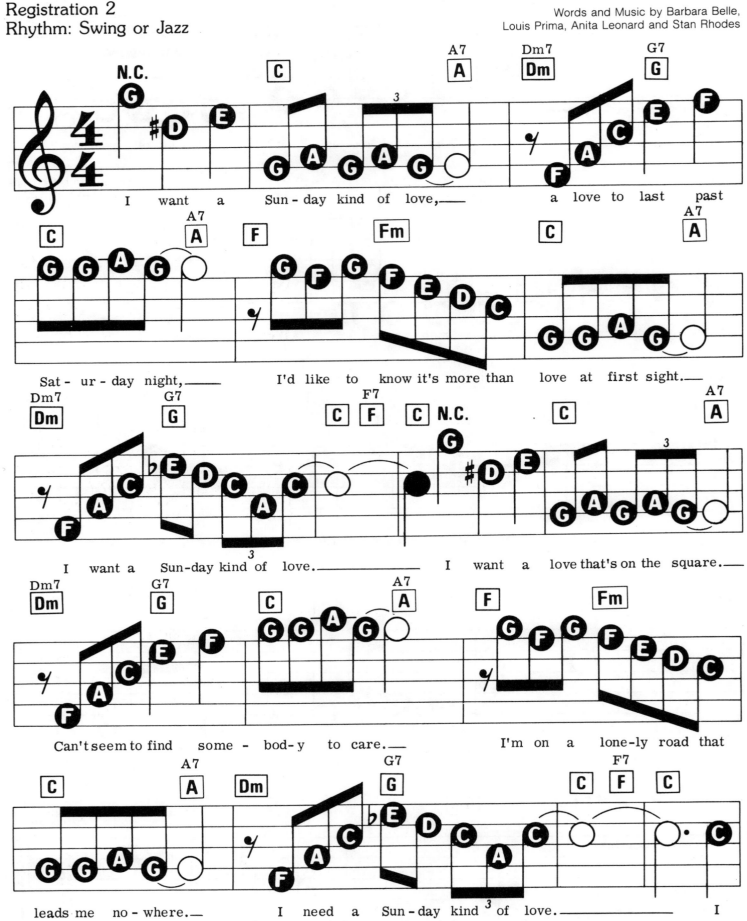

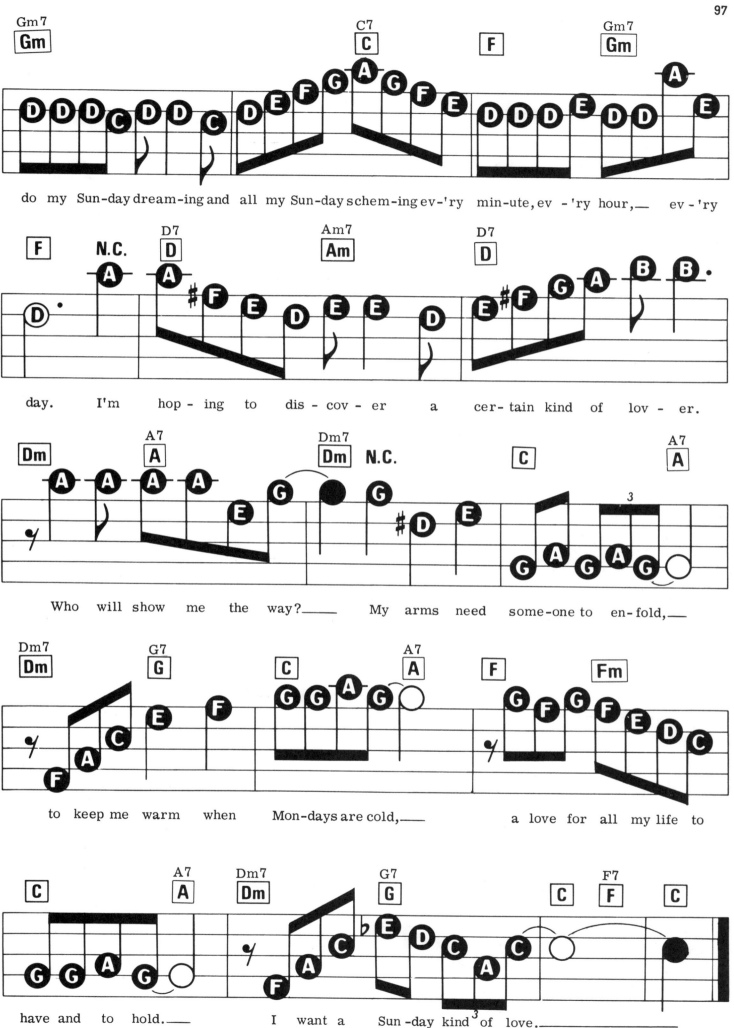

Take the "A" Train

Registration 4
Rhythm: Swing or Big Band

Words and Music by
Billy Strayhorn

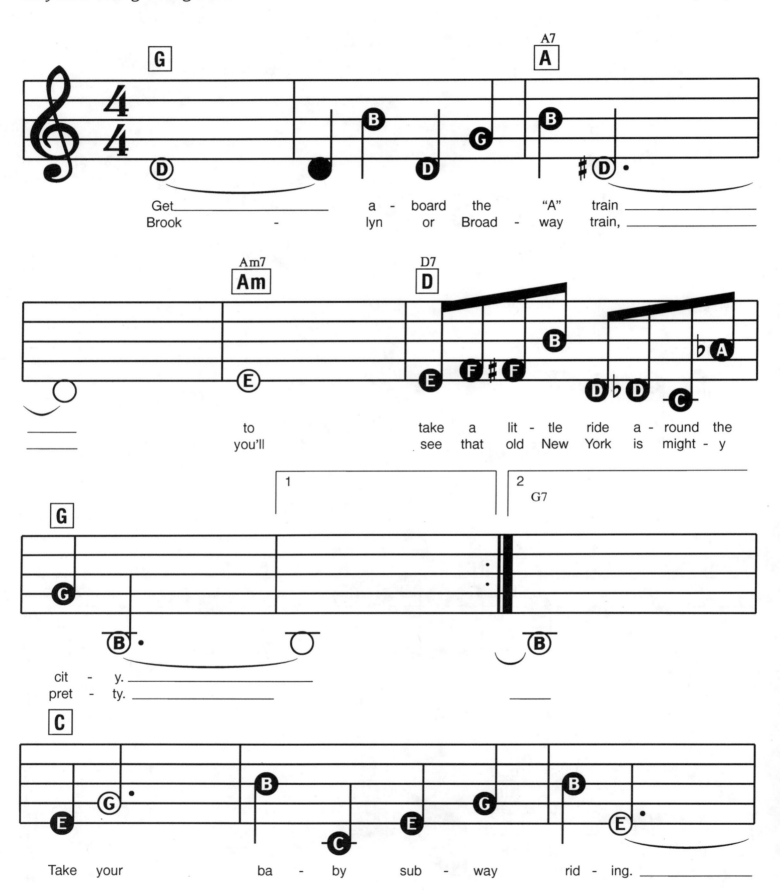

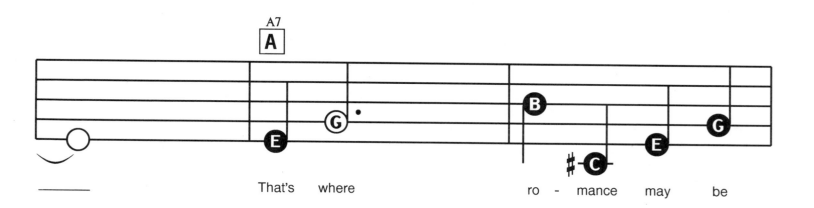

That's where ro - mance may be

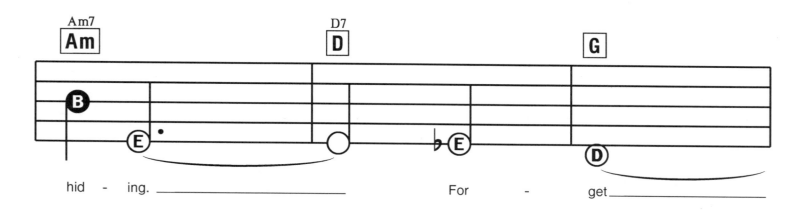

hid - ing. _____ For - get _____

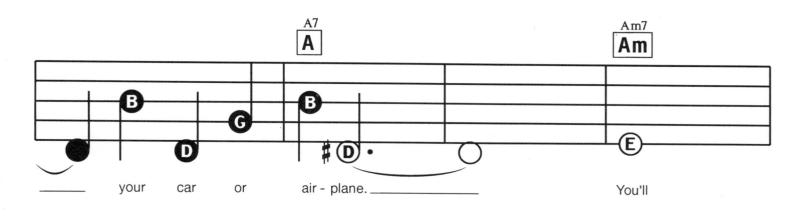

_____ your car or air - plane. _____ You'll

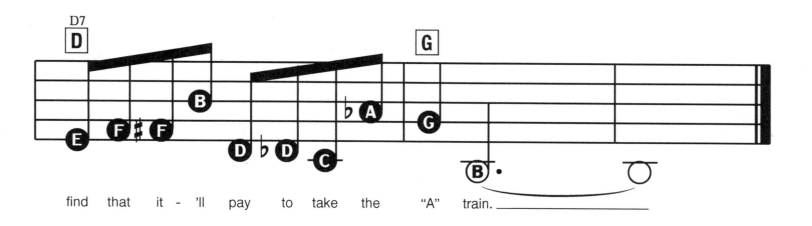

find that it - 'll pay to take the "A" train. _____

Taking a Chance on Love

Registration 7
Rhythm: Fox Trot or Swing

Words by John La Touche and Ted Fetter
Music by Vernon Duke

Tangerine

from the Paramount Picture THE FLEET'S IN

Registration 9
Rhythm: Fox Trot or Swing

Words by Johnny Mercer
Music by Victor Schertzinger

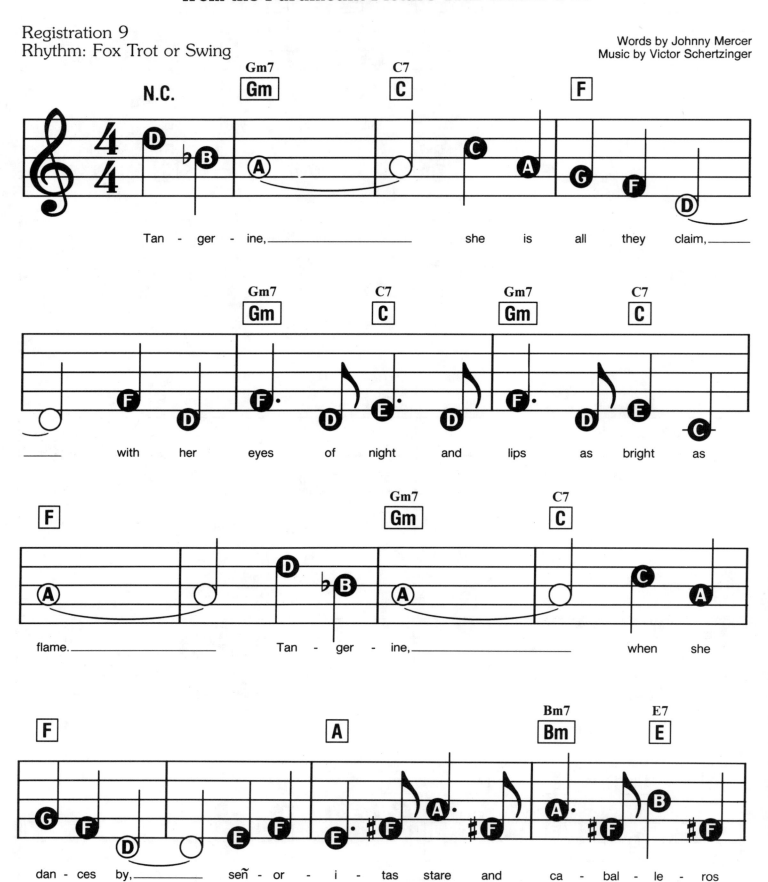

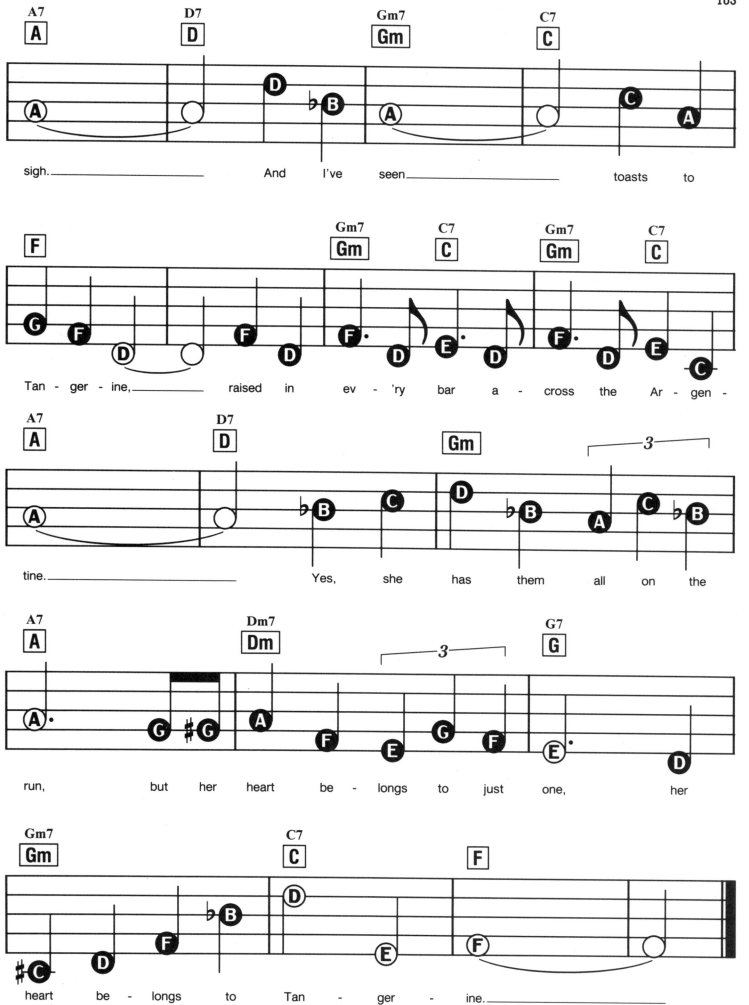

That Old Black Magic
from the Paramount Picture STAR SPANGLED RHYTHM

Registration 1
Rhythm: Fox Trot or Swing

Words by Johnny Mercer
Music by Harold Arlen

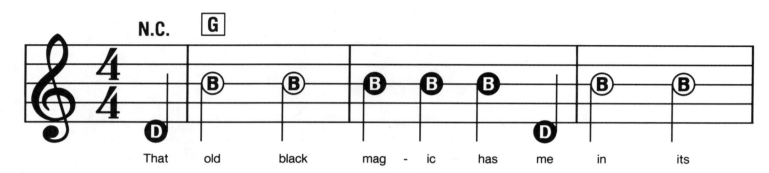

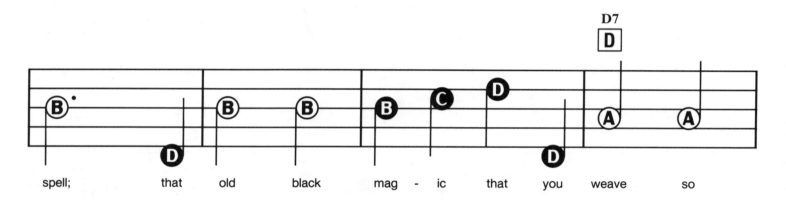

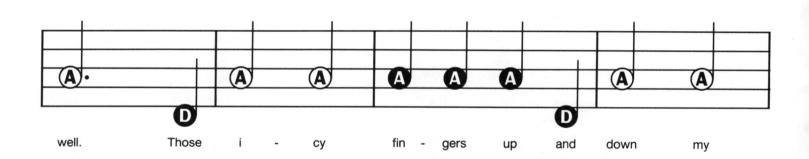

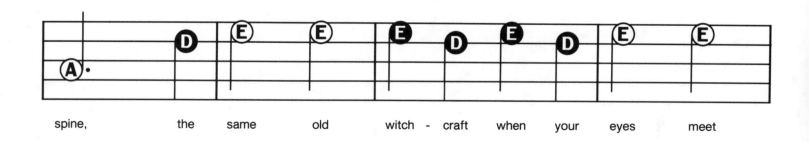

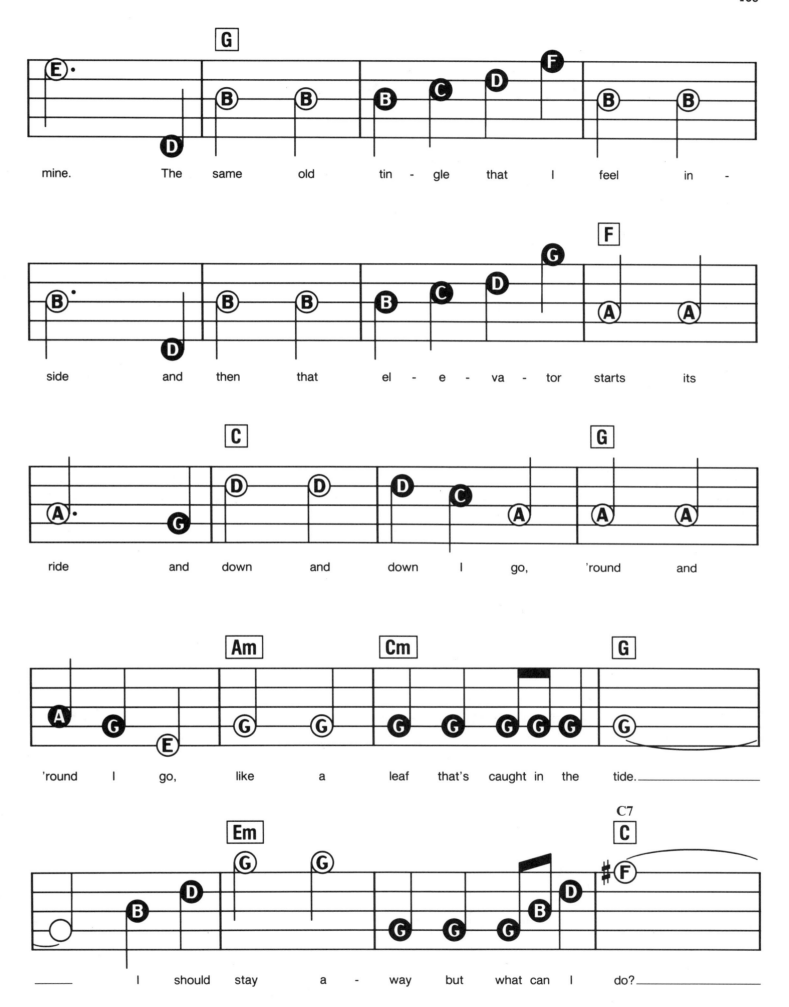

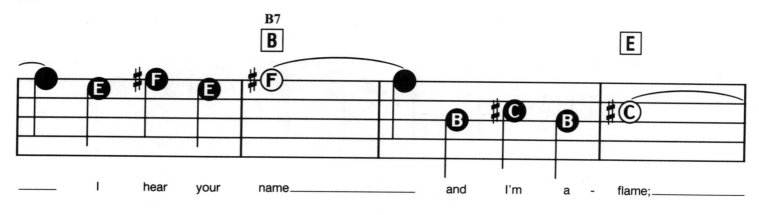

I hear your name and I'm a - flame;

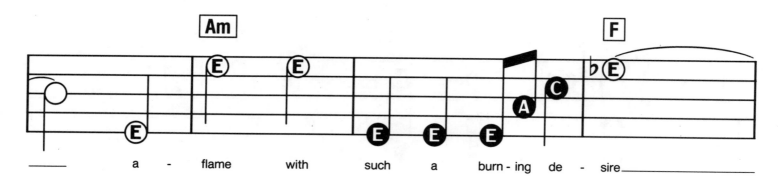

a - flame with such a burn - ing de - sire

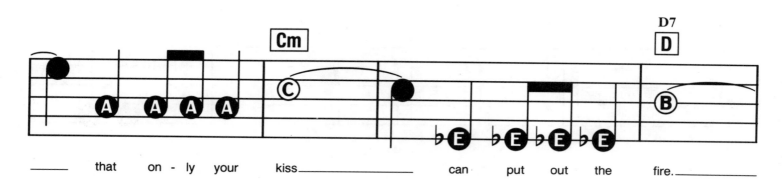

that on - ly your kiss can put out the fire.

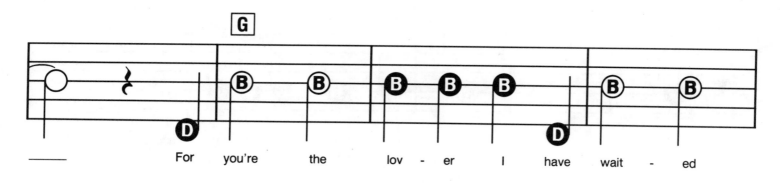

For you're the lov - er I have wait - ed

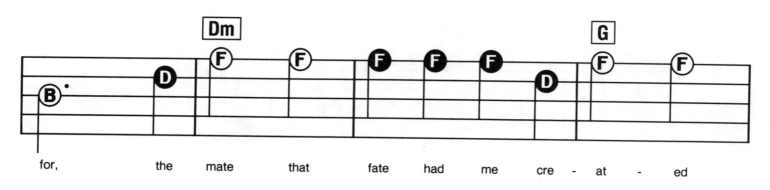

for, the mate that fate had me cre - at - ed

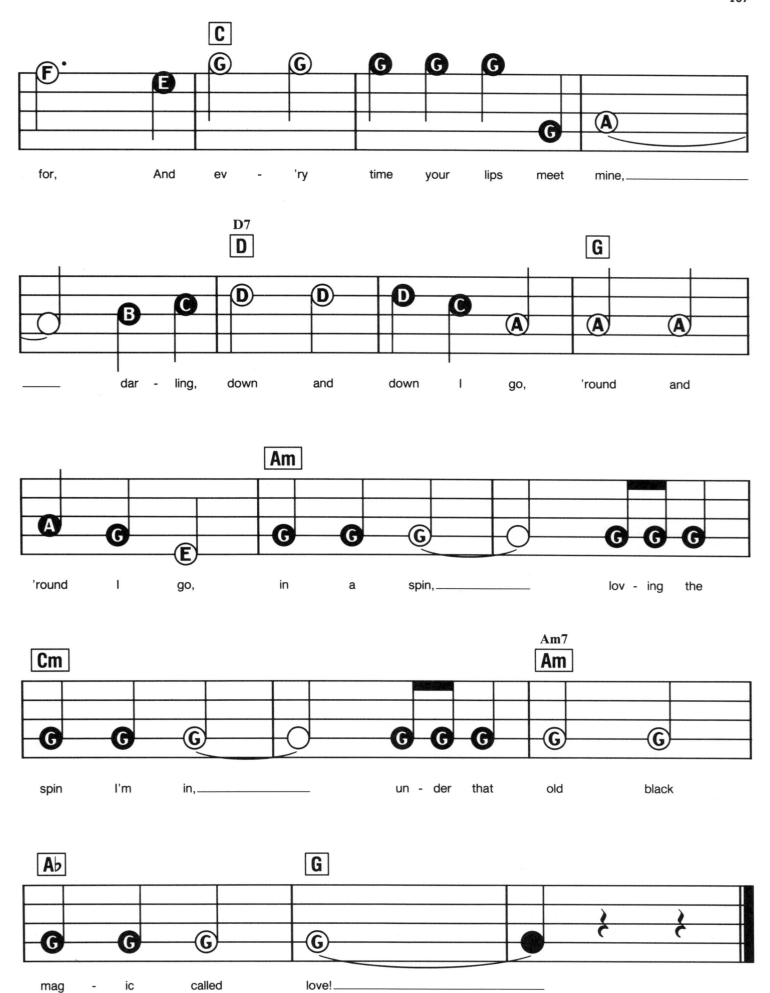

Tuxedo Junction

Registration 1
Rhythm: Fox Trot or Swing

Words by Buddy Feyne
Music by Erskine Hawkins,
William Johnson and Julian Dash

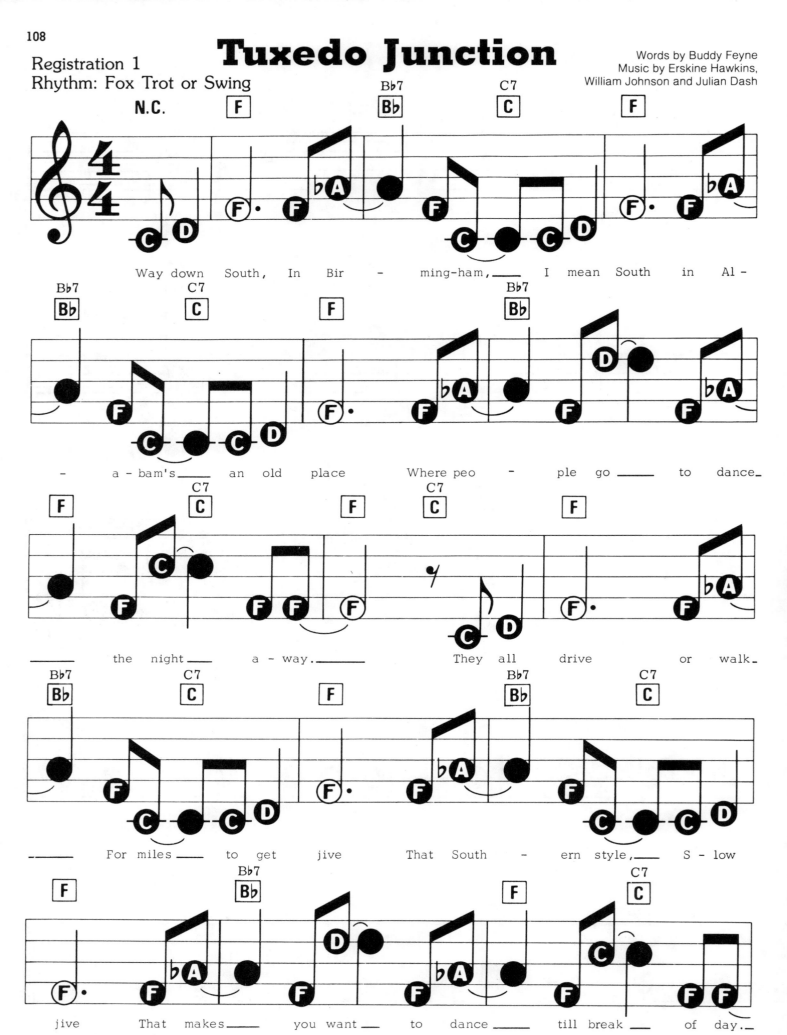

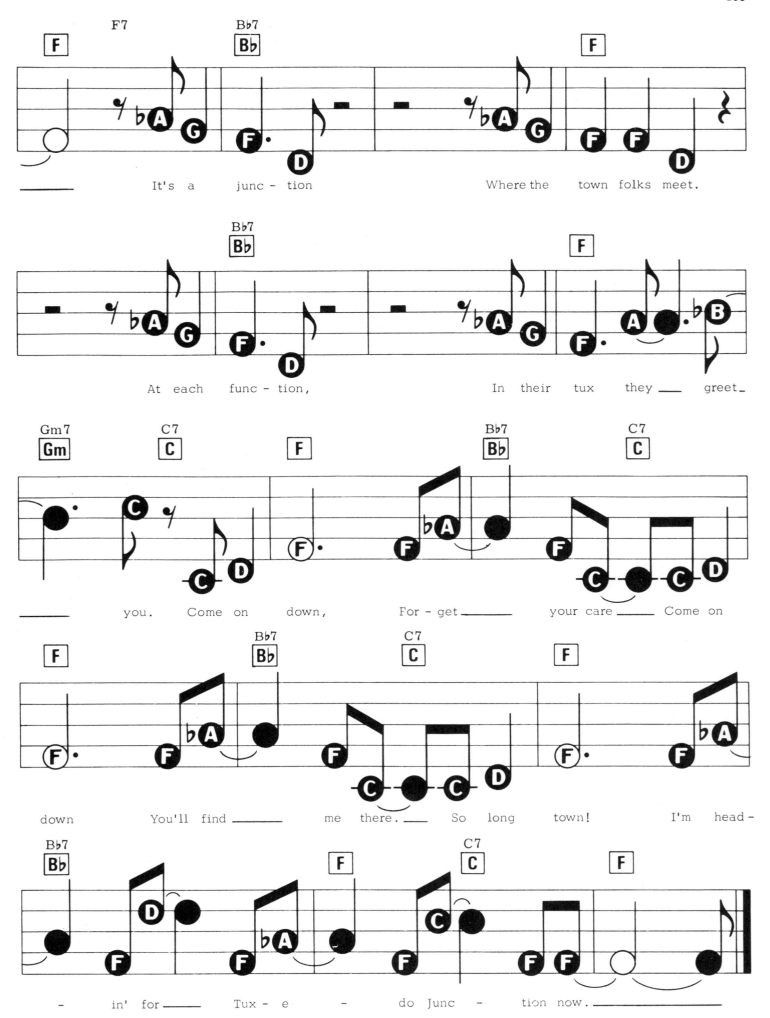

You'll Never Walk Alone
from CAROUSEL

Words by Oscar Hammerstein II
Music by Richard Rodgers

Registration 5
Rhythm: Ballad

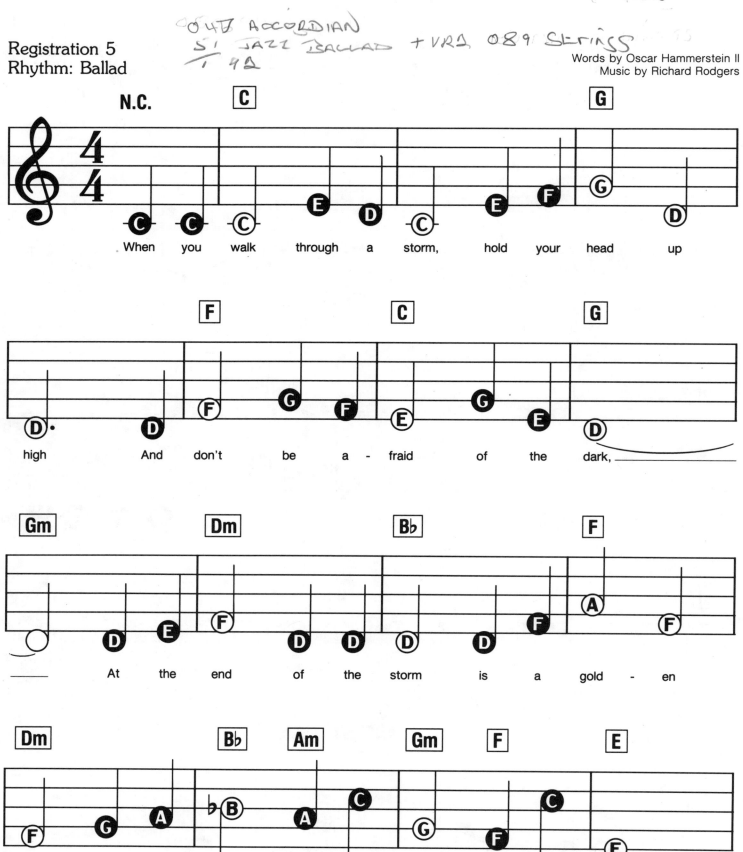

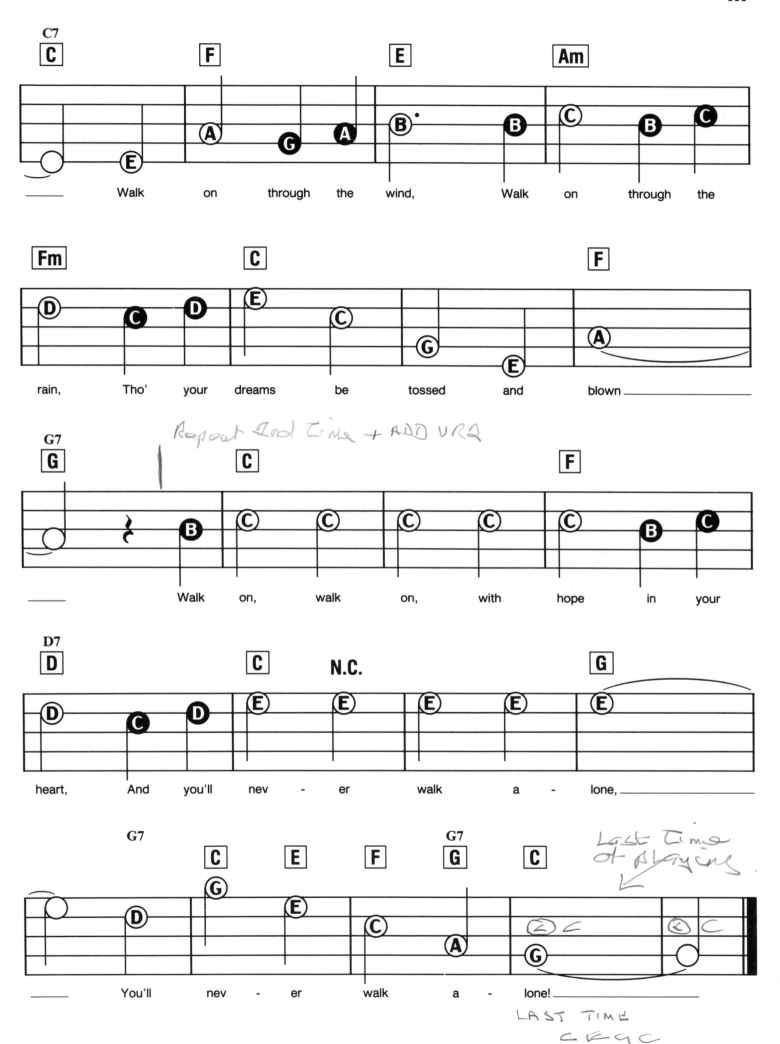

111

Younger than Springtime
from SOUTH PACIFIC

Registration 4
Rhythm: Swing or Fox Trot

Lyrics by Oscar Hammerstein II
Music by Richard Rodgers

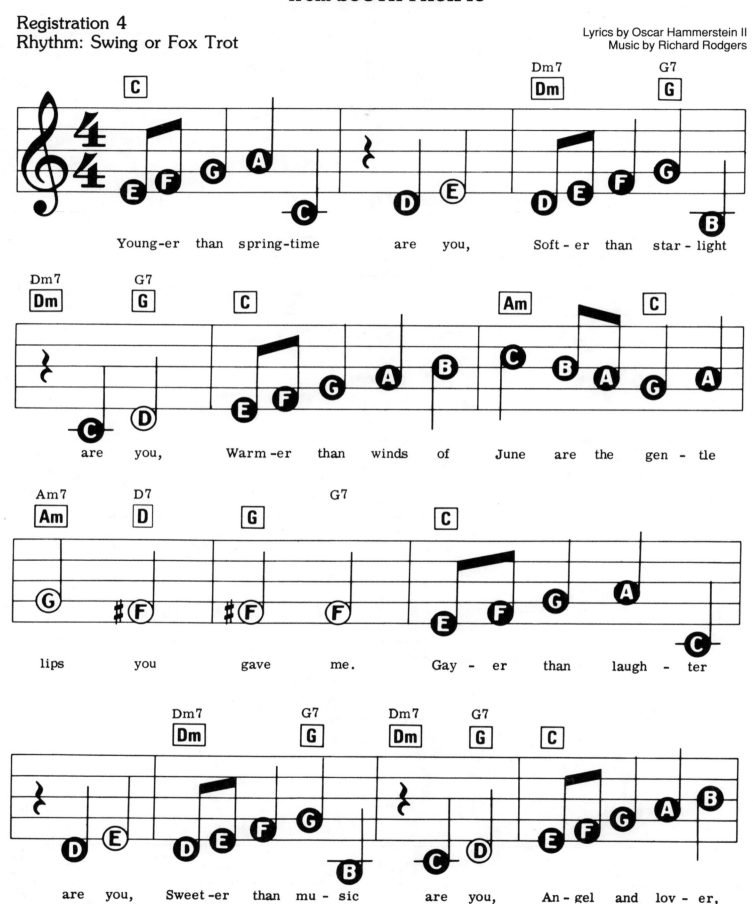

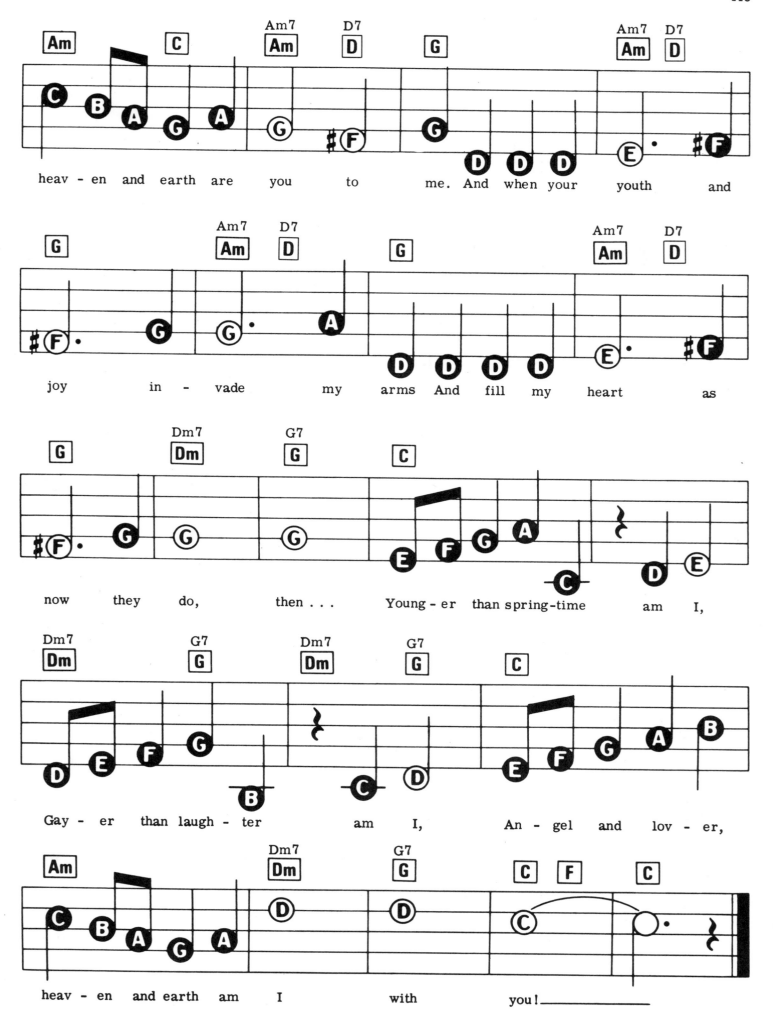

Zip-A-Dee-Doo-Dah
from Walt Disney's SONG OF THE SOUTH

Registration 8
Rhythm: Fox Trot or Swing

Words by Ray Gilbert
Music by Allie Wrubel

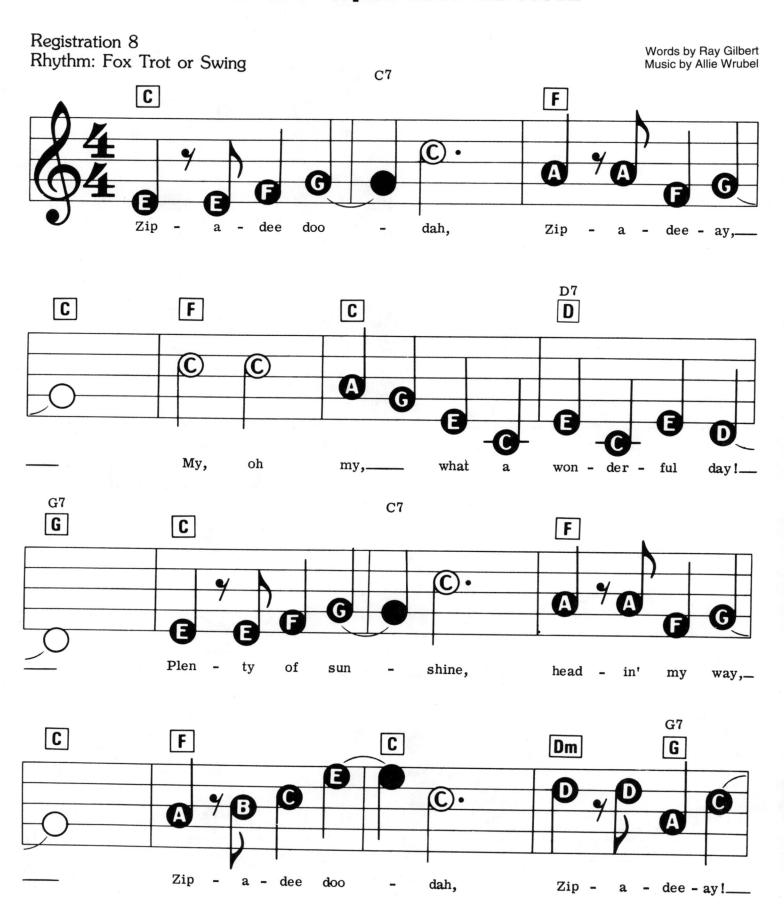

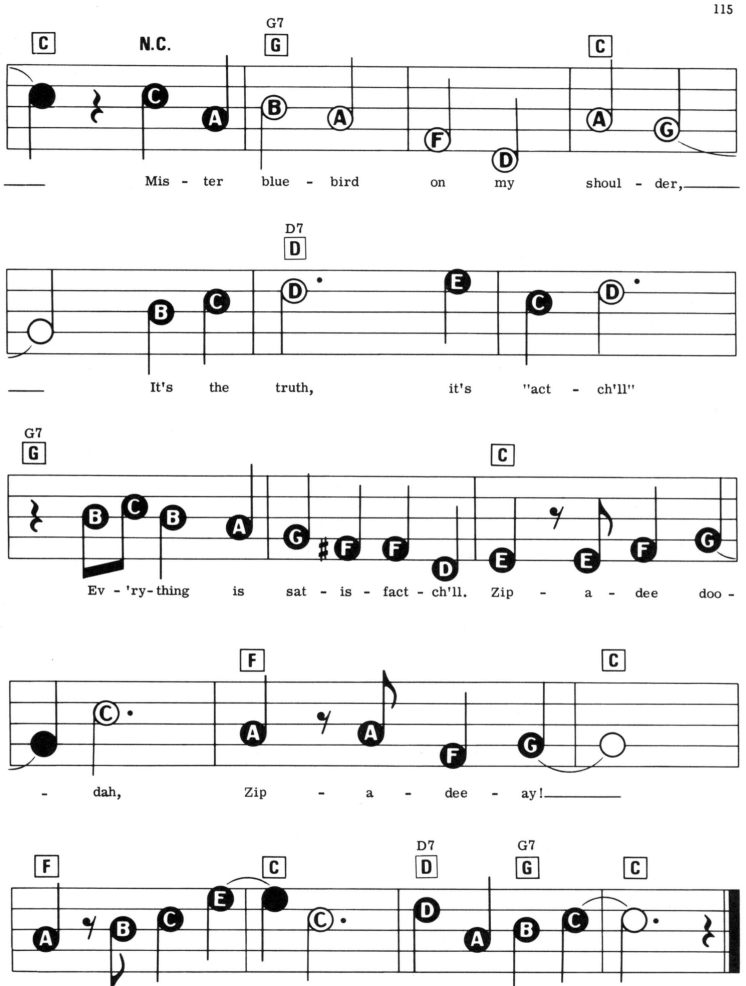

There! I've Said It Again

Registration 7
Rhythm: Swing or Shuffle

Words by Dave Mann
Music by Redd Evans

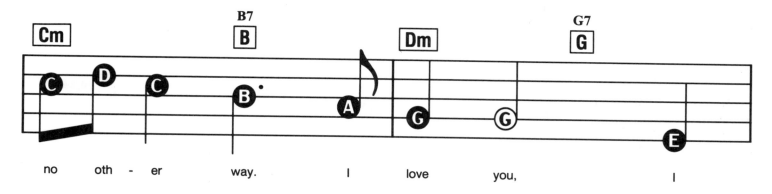

no oth - er way. I love you, I

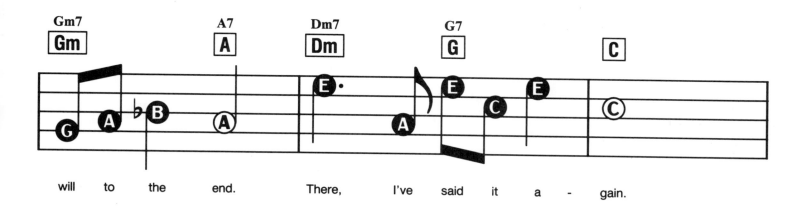

will to the end. There, I've said it a - gain.

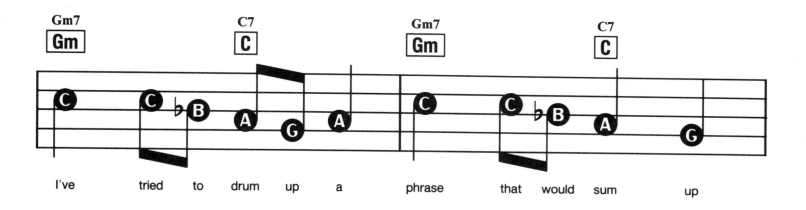

I've tried to drum up a phrase that would sum up

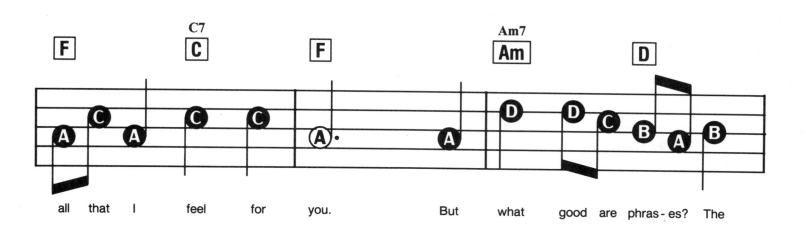

all that I feel for you. But what good are phras - es? The

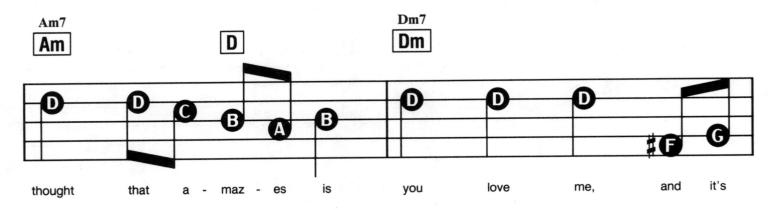

thought that a - maz - es is you love me, and it's

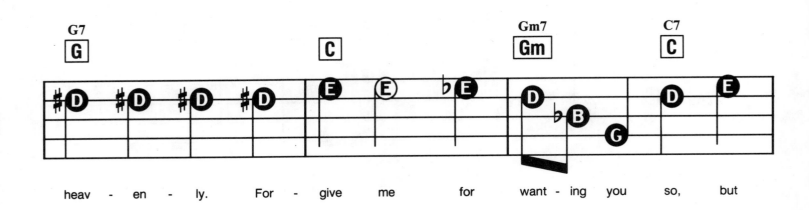

heav - en - ly. For - give me for want - ing you so, but

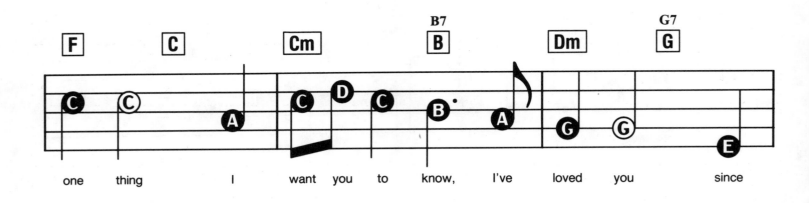

one thing I want you to know, I've loved you since

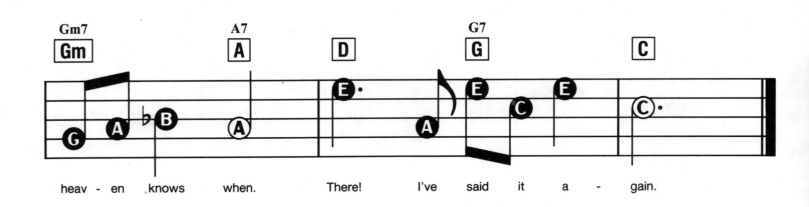

heav - en knows when. There! I've said it a - gain.